It's another Quality Book from CGP

This book is for anyone getting ready for the KS3 English SATs.

It contains lots of tricky questions designed to make you sweat — because that's the only way you'll get any better.

It's also got some daft bits in to try and make the whole experience at least vaguely entertaining for you.

What CGP is all about

Our sole aim here at CGP is to produce the highest quality books — carefully written, immaculately presented and dangerously close to being funny.

Then we work our socks off to get them out to you — at the cheapest possible prices.

Contents

THE READING TEST

THE WRITING TEST

THE SHAKESPEARE TEST

ANSWERS

Published by Coordination Group Publications, Ltd.

Contributors:

Taissa Csáky   Chris Dennett   Tim Major   Katherine Reed   Ed Robinson

ISBN: 978 1 84762 170 2

Groovy website: www.cgpbooks.co.uk

Jolly bits of clipart from CorelDRAW®

Printed by Elanders Hindson Ltd, Newcastle upon Tyne

With thanks to Paula Barnett, Ed Robinson, Glenn Rogers, Rachel Selway and Dan Owen for the proofreading.

Finding Facts

There's always a tasty bunch of fact-finding questions in the SATs. You just have to find the right bit in the text and write down the info — you couldn't ask for a nicer start to the SATs really.

An extract from a magazine article about the PB Animation Studio

The PB Animation Studio was founded in 1998 by Managing Director Paul Black, and since then it has become a hugely successful business. In the beginning, it was just Paul working alone in his attic room, but now the company employs 230 people in jobs ranging from scriptwriters to cooks!

The secret of PB's success has always been the quality of its 3-D animation. Characters are carefully shaped from ordinary modelling clay, and are usually no more than 20 centimetres tall. More complex characters have wire frames (or rod-and-joint structures called armatures) inside the clay. These allow the model to be adjusted very accurately.

The really time-consuming part of the job is actually filming — in order for the characters' movements to appear realistic, 24 pictures (or 'frames') need to be taken to put together 1 second of finished film!

Q1 Copy and complete the table using information from the magazine article above.

Description	Fact
Year PB Animation Studio was created	
Founded by...	
Paul Black's current position	
Total number of employees today	

Q2 What is the normal maximum height of PB's characters?

Q3 What must be included in models that need very accurate adjustment?

Q4 What are 'armatures'?

Q5 How many frames per second need to be filmed? Choose from options i)-iv).

i) 20 ii) 230 iii) 24 iv) 25

Q6 Why is this number of frames per second needed?

You don't need to write loads — just write out the bit of the text that answers the question.

Q7 According to the writer, what is the secret of PB's success?

Finding the Important Bits

The first thing to do with any reading question is to dig out the bit of the text that tells you the answer to the question. Then lick it clean and give it a good chew. Or just write it down.

An extract from the story *Carrie's Life of Piracy*

Carrie darted round the corner into a dingy side street full of discarded wooden crates. She was closely followed by Ben, who stopped and bent over, panting. He felt like he'd been out of breath ever since they'd left the Pirate Academy.

"Come on, Ben! We have to keep moving — otherwise they'll send us back, and you know what that means..."

Suddenly they were aware of a shadow looming over them. Carrie gasped and looked up towards the leering, cruel face of Captain Hack.

"Aaah, my dear pupils," said Hack, relishing each word, "I'm only performing my duty as your tutor. You know that any student failing to hand in homework must walk the plank."

Carrie and Ben exchanged a glance. Ben dashed forward with a yell, and managed to slip between Captain Hack's legs. Before Hack could react, Ben ripped a thin plank of wood from a nearby crate.

"Carrie! Catch!" he shouted, and tossed the plank over Hack's head, to be caught by Carrie.

For a moment Carrie looked at the plank, bemused. Then she remembered her sword-fighting lessons, and crouched with the plank in her hand, ready to defend herself against her pirate tutor.

Q1 Write out the part of the text where you are told about the following things.

a) Where Carrie and Ben arrive at the start of the extract.
b) How Ben feels at the beginning of the extract.
c) Where Carrie and Ben have come from.
d) What Captain Hack looks like.
e) How Captain Hack wants to punish Carrie and Ben.
f) What Carrie and Ben did that needs to be punished.
g) How Ben escapes from Captain Hack.
h) Where Ben got the thin plank of wood from.

Umm... I'd better head back. Reports to write, homework to mark...

Q2 How do Carrie and Ben know that Captain Hack has arrived? Write out the part of the text that tells you.

Q3 What is Carrie about to do with the thin plank of wood? Write out the part of the text that tells you.

Trapped in a snow poem — it was phrasing...

If you can pick out useful phrases from texts really quickly, then you'll have bags of time left for important things like looking out of the window and picking your nose. And answering questions.

Backing Up Points

You have to back up your answers, otherwise you haven't proved they're right.
The trick is to always make a COMMENT, give EVIDENCE from the text, then EXPLAIN what it means.

Questions 1-3 are about the following short extract.

"I think we should get rid of the whole stinking lot," said Hanif, pointing at the rabbits.

Q1 Write a sentence commenting on how Hanif feels about the rabbits.

Q2 Which of the following sentences uses evidence from the extract to show how Hanif feels about the rabbits?

i) Hanif wants to get rid of the rabbits.

ii) Hanif wants to get rid of the rabbits. He shouts, which shows he doesn't like them.

iii) Hanif wants to get rid of the rabbits. He calls them "stinking", which shows that he doesn't like them.

Q3 What does this tell the reader about Hanif? Copy out the correct answer.

i) Hanif has a strong opinion about the rabbits.

ii) Hanif is depressed and hates everything in the world.

iii) Hanif is a bully who goes around annoying other people.

Questions 4-6 are about the extract below.

Milla glanced around the street nervously before she dumped the envelope into the bin.

Q4 What is Milla's mood in this extract?

Q5 Write out the part of the text that backs up your answer to Q4.

Q6 What does this tell the reader about Milla? Copy out the correct answer.

i) Milla doesn't like using bins in the street.

ii) Milla seems to be worried that someone will see her dumping the envelope into the bin.

iii) Milla doesn't care what anyone thinks about her dumping the envelope into the bin.

Question 7 is about the extract below.

"I'll be fine — don't worry about me," said Miles, with the hint of a tear in his eye.

Q7 How is Miles feeling in this extract? Write about Miles' character in your answer. Give evidence from the text in your answer and explain how it proves your point.

Summarising

If you're asked to summarise the points made in a text, it means that you need to write the important bits out in your own words. And don't waffle — summarising means using less words.

An extract from the story *Felix and the Dragon's Revenge*

The elderly King looked down his nose at the men assembled before him.

"Do you mean to tell me that they *all* went free?" he thundered.

Felix remained on his knees and let out a gentle sob. The King, becoming somewhat reflective, turned and gazed vacantly out of the tall window.

"It wasn't always like this," he muttered. "During the reign of my father, captured knights had some respect and *stayed* captured. Aaah, my father. What it was to be a child. I used to play in that very garden. Haha! The fun I had with my wooden horse... Ahem. Anyway, it just won't do, there have been too many daring escapes recently."

Felix was about to interrupt, but the King's courtier placed a hand on his shoulder to stop him.

"And you," began the King, his voiced raised and turning to face Felix, "You have done nothing to stop these knights!" He gestured to Prime Minister Katan. "Tie Felix up, take him to Vertis Ledge, and let the dragons do as they wish."

As Felix was being dragged away by two burly attendants, he found the strength to cry out, "You'll see, my lord! One of these days the dragons will come after you!"

Q1 Make a list of all the characters mentioned in the text.

Hint: some of the characters' names aren't given.

Q2 Which of the characters actually speak in the text?

Q3 Copy out and correct this summary of the paragraph starting "It wasn't always like this..."

The King remembers when his father was king, and knights were harder to control. He decides that something must be done about the knights. Then he starts to think about his childhood when he played with his toys in the garden.

Hint: There are two big errors.

Q4 Copy out the sentence that describes the King's mood in the fourth paragraph.

i) He seems angry with Felix, and keeps shouting at him.

ii) He seems angry with Felix, but is easily distracted by memories of his childhood.

iii) He talks about his childhood and doesn't care about the knights at all.

Q5 Summarise the paragraph starting "And you," in your own words.

Q6 Write a summary of the whole text. Your summary should be no more than five sentences long, and you'll have to decide which of the details on this page need to be included.

In winter I yodel — in summar i sing...

Summarising is dead handy even if a question doesn't ask you to do it specifically. If you're grappling with a nightmare text, try retelling the story to yourself, as simply as you can.

Different Types of Text

As soon as you start reading a text in the SATs you should be thinking about what type of text it is. Then straightaway you'll be thinking about the kind of questions they'll ask.

A

Five per cent of the population will suffer from an epileptic seizure at some time in their life, *writes Gareth Johns*. Epilepsy affects 450,000 people in the UK, usually under-20-year-olds and those over 60. Seizures involve loss of consciousness and may affect memory or mood.

B

Watching the tutting clock,
Only six more minutes until I can be
there and not *here*.
Gazing out through dusty panes,
Following the inkblot shadows of
clouds with my eyes.
Outside, sunlight plays on the ground
like excitable children,
And a bird shouts with happiness.

C

Toby proceeded to mow the lawn like a man resigned to a long stretch in prison.

Being a man of unimaginable dullness, his only reaction when his wife bellowed that she was leaving him was to gently let the engine sputter to a forlorn halt. All that remained was a glacial silence, and a partially cut lawn.

D

In order to get the best results from your T-300 kitchen juicer, please note the following points:

1) **Always make a clear space around the T-300 in case of juice spray.**
2) **Avoid juicing soft fruits such as bananas. The residue may be difficult to clear from the workings of the T-300.**

Q1 Copy out each title below and write down which of the texts each goes with — A, B, C or D.

Epilepsy — The Facts   Using your T-300   Waiting   A Man Alone

Q2 Which texts are examples of non-fiction?

Q3 Which texts feature very descriptive language?

Q4 Write out each of the labels below and decide whether they apply to A, B, C or D.

Poem   Story   Manual   Magazine article

Q5 Match each of the questions below to one of the texts — A, B, C or D.

a) Describe the ways that the writer has made his points clear in the text.
b) Explain how the writer contrasts indoors and outdoors in the text.
c) How does the writer use facts and figures to back up his points?
d) How does the writer show that the main character is lonely?

You don't actually have to do the questions.

Working Out What's Going On

The texts in the SATs aren't always that easy — some of them are downright confusing. Examiners often ask you to work out what's happened or what might happen next.

An extract from the short story *Mrs Hanrahan's Holiday*

Ever since she'd woken to shrill beeps that still echoed around her head, Mrs Hanrahan's day had got worse and worse. She'd had to spend a few hours hunting for the tickets — knowing that without them she *definitely* wouldn't be going on holiday today. She'd finally located the tickets beneath the tottering pile of dirty dishes, but hadn't retrieved them safely before sacrificing two of the dishes to the floor in a flurry of ceramic and congealed Chinese takeaway.

Finally, Mrs Hanrahan was ready.

"Bags packed – check. Tickets – check. House keys – check," she murmured. She placed the front door keys carefully on top of the tickets. With a grimace, Mrs Hanrahan suddenly remembered to put the milk bottles outside. She abandoned her luggage, collected the bottles, wrote a quick note to the milkman and then ventured outside. Just as she placed the bottles by the front doormat, Mrs Hanrahan was aware of the sound of the front door latch clicking behind her...

Q1 Copy and complete this table to show the order of the events in the extract.

Event	Order in extract
Looks for tickets	
Puts milk bottles outside	
Wakes up	1
Has an accident in the kitchen	
Puts front door keys with tickets	

Q2 Write out the part of the text that gives you a clue about what kind of tickets Mrs Hanrahan is searching for.

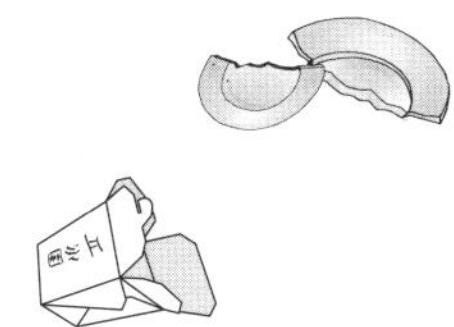

Q3 Write out the part of the text that tells you about the accident in the first paragraph.

Q4 Copy out the answer that best describes the accident.

i) Mrs Hanrahan ate some Chinese takeaway, and then dropped a plate.

ii) Mrs Hanrahan knocked over two dirty dishes, and they smashed on the floor.

iii) Mrs Hanrahan knocked over two dirty dishes, and they landed in the bin.

Q5 What happens as Mrs Hanrahan is putting the milk bottles outside?

Q6 Write a paragraph explaining what you think might happen next in the story.

Working Out What's Going On

Questions that ask you to work out what's happening can also refer to non-fiction texts. Sometimes you need to work out what technical language means, by looking at the sentences around it.

An extract from a magazine article about manual photography

Many of us are used to just pointing, pressing, and getting someone else to do the dirty work. However, using manual cameras takes a bit more thought and preparation. Are you up to the challenge?

Firstly, you need to decide what type of film to use. 'Slow' films are suitable for normal lighting, whereas you'll need to use a faster ISO 400 film to take pictures on gloomy days (or as fast as ISO 1000 if it's night-time).

Once you've loaded the film, you've got to think about camera settings before you start snapping. Changing the aperture setting affects the amount of light that comes into the camera — if it's a bright scene then make the aperture narrower, if it's a dark scene then the aperture needs to be larger.

Next comes shutter speed settings (the amount of time the shutter stays open when you press the button). A long shutter speed not only lets in a lot of light, it also means that any moving objects will be blurred — useful for arty action shots but not so good if you want lots of fine detail. If you're not using a camera with automatic focus, you'll need to rotate the focusing ring before you take the picture.

Of course, the next step is getting the pictures developed — you can either send the film away to a laboratory, or you can develop the pictures yourself in a darkroom.

Next week — darkroom secrets

Q1 What does 'pointing, pressing, and getting someone else to do the dirty work' in the introduction to the text mean?

Q2 Which of the things below explains what ISO refers to? Write out the bit of text that tells you.

film size | film speed | lighting conditions | sugary sports drinks

Q3 Which of the film speeds below is a 'slow' film? Explain how you worked it out.

ISO 1000 | ISO 400 | ISO 100 | ISO 1600

Q4 What do you think the line 'Next week — darkroom secrets' refers to?

Q5 David wants to take detailed action pictures of a sports day outside in the sunlight. Copy this table and fill it in to show the settings that David should use.

Camera setting	Set to...	Reason
Film speed		
Aperture setting		
Shutter speed		

Q6 Emily wants to take blurry pictures of a jazz band playing in a dingy bar. Draw a table similar to the one in Q5 and fill it in to show the settings that she should use.

Q7 SAT-STYLE QUESTION Why do you think the writer has described using manual cameras as a 'challenge'? Write a paragraph, and refer to the extract to back up your answer. (5 marks)

Working Out How Characters Feel

Examiners also like asking you about how characters feel about what's happening. You need to put yourself in the character's shoes for a bit, and hope that they're not full of toe jam.

An extract from the story *Sir Lancelot's Quest*

Sir Lancelot sighed deeply and gazed upward at the falcon circling overhead. It was free to soar where it wished, whereas he had to trudge grimly ahead through the forest, towards Camelot and the king he had wished never to see again. All of a sudden, fatigue hit him. The battle with Sir Phelot had been a hard one, and now Sir Lancelot almost wished that he himself had been slain, if only to be finally at peace.

The journey had been long and difficult. Many times Lancelot had been forced to hack his way wearily through dense foliage with his sword, had waded through rivers and then walked for hours in sodden clothes, and had bloodied his hands from battles with countless honourable knights.

Q1 Write out the part of the text that tells you why Lancelot doesn't want to go to Camelot.

Q2 Copy out the answer that best describes why Sir Lancelot is jealous of the falcon.

i) Lancelot wishes he was free to go where he wanted and didn't have to walk any more.

ii) Lancelot wishes he could fly to Camelot instead of walking.

iii) Lancelot wishes he could get a better view from above the trees.

Q3 The extract starts "Sir Lancelot sighed deeply". Write down two other things Lancelot does that show how he is feeling.

Hi Arthur, mate, sos about that thing with your wife... No. Sorry Arthur, please believe me... No.

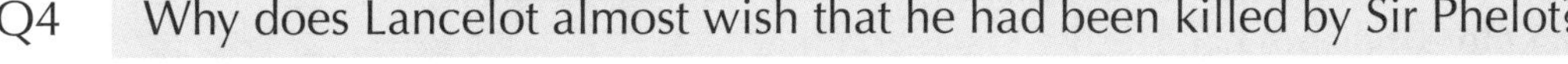

Q4 Why does Lancelot almost wish that he had been killed by Sir Phelot?

Q5 Match up the things that happened on the journey, to how they would have made Lancelot feel.

What happened	How it would have made Lancelot feel
Had to cut through dense foliage	Sad because he respected them
Waded through rivers and walked in wet clothes	Tired and frustrated
Killed many other knights	Uncomfortable

Q6 Write a paragraph explaining how you think Sir Lancelot would have felt at the end of his journey to Camelot. Use your answers to the other questions to back up your points.

How to get rid of boils — Lancelot...

The questions on the last three pages are all about ways of figuring out what's happening in texts that aren't 100% clear. Questions like these always come up in the SATs, so get practising now.

Descriptions

Exam questions often ask you to write about the way things are described in the text. You've got to be able to work out what information a description gives you, and the effect it has on the reader.

An extract from the novella *The Case of the Missing Relic*

Tonight, the whole city seemed peaceful. Even the birds were asleep, and not a sound disturbed the eerie quiet. The river flowed gently past the houses as if it didn't want to wake up the slumbering inhabitants.

Inspector Graham paced the streets, expecting trouble at any moment. He gazed up at the pale moon which lit the streets below, and held his gas lamp out with a trembling hand. In front of him he could make out the grey archway of a narrow doorway. The night before he had come across a pack of snarling dogs guarding the doorway, but tonight they were absent. The door opened with a low creak at his push, and the lamp cast a flickering glow over the dim inside of the room. The only furniture was a broad farmhouse table, upon which were several items — a cotton glove, a faded yellow sheet of paper, and a small stone carving of a man crouching as if about to pounce at the Inspector.

Q1 Copy and complete the table about the way things are described in the extract above.

Thing being described	How it's described
	Peaceful
	Flickering
The doorway	
The dogs guarding the doorway	
	Faded and yellow
Inspector Graham's hand	
The inside of the room	

Q2 Which of the descriptions from the table in Q1 make the things sound scary?

Q3 Write out the part of the text that describes the stone carving.

Q4 Write out the statement that explains the effect of the description in Q3.

i) The statue is described as if it is alive — this effect is called alliteration.

ii) The statue is described as if it is alive — this effect is called metaphor.

iii) The statue is described as if it is alive — this effect is called personification.

Q5 Write out another part of the text that uses the same effect.

Q6 SAT-STYLE QUESTION How does the writer of *The Case of the Missing Relic* use descriptions to make the story scary? Use your answers to the questions on this page to help you. (5 marks)

Descriptions of Characters

Writers tell you about characters through the way they're described — the things they say and the things they do. I bet you can spot descriptions a mile away, but practise writing about them too.

An extract from the novel *The Movie Murders*

"...and cut!"

David Hodgson had been directing his film *Curl Girl* for almost eight months now, and it was beginning to get the better of him. He wheeled around abruptly on his heel towards his fresh-faced assistant Sarah, who surveyed him with a slightly pitying look.

"Have the extras arrived yet?" asked David in a shaky voice. He grabbed Sarah by the lapels of her smart jacket. Sarah tried to keep smiling, but failed. "And *where* is our leading lady?" demanded David, as he started to pull at the few tufts of greying hair left on his head, his eyes darting from side to side as if following the path of a wasp.

"Your ravishing, immensely talented leading lady has just entered the building," said a silky voice from the darkness. A figure sauntered casually into the light — it was none other than Denise Penrith. She tossed back her mane of honey-coloured hair and fixed David with a commanding gaze. Denise continued in a steady, alluring tone, "and I would like to talk to you about my fees."

Q1 Write out the sentence which describes how Sarah feels about David Hodgson.

i) Sarah hates David and tries to make life unpleasant for him.

ii) Sarah seems to feel sorry for David and tries to keep him happy.

iii) Sarah is madly in love with David and would do anything to make him happy.

Q2 Copy out two parts of the text that back up your answer.

Q3 For each of the three characters, pick out two words below that sum them up.

arrogant short-tempered sympathetic stressed stunning tolerant

Q4 For each of your choices in Q3, write down a phrase from the text that backs up your answer.

Q5 What do the words 'she tossed back her mane of honey-coloured hair' tell you about Denise?

There are three important bits in the phrase — 'tossed', 'mane' and 'honey-coloured'.

Q6 Why do you think the writer used the word 'sauntered' instead of 'walked'?

Q7 Describe the ways that the writer of *The Movie Murders* contrasts characters through descriptions. Use your answers to the questions on this page to help you. (5 marks)

SAT-STYLE QUESTION

I'm ready for my close-up now...

Always remember to back up your points with evidence from the text. It's no good saying that 'Denise is a stuck-up old witch' if you can't prove it using the text. Even if it's true.

Similes and Metaphors

Writers often use comparisons to make their descriptions more vivid.
The two main types of comparison you need to know here, are similes and metaphors.

A gig review from a music newspaper

Any really great rock band knows that you have to keep your audience waiting. By the time The Brums arrived on stage, the audience were howling like wolves. Right from the start, singer Leo Ryder was a monster, roaring into the microphone. Guitarist Arnie X was possessed by the ghost of Jimi Hendrix as he played the most frantic guitar solos this side of Wigan. Jay Bryson beat the drums as if they were fires to be put out, but somehow managed to keep time as faithfully as an honest referee.

As soon as the band launched into their number 2 hit, 'The First Rule is...', the audience were like a seething wave of noise. If it wasn't already clear, this concert proves that The Brums are the heavyweight boxers of rock music — and they certainly don't pull any punches.

Q1 Write 'metaphor', 'simile' or 'neither' next to each of these phrases.

a) you have to keep your audience waiting
b) the audience were like a seething wave of noise
c) The Brums are the heavyweight boxers of rock music

Similes say that something is like something else. Metaphors say that something is something else.

Q2 Which of these answers best explains why the writer describes the audience as 'howling like wolves'?

i) The shouting audience sounded quiet and tuneful, like wolf howls.
ii) The shouting audience sounded noisy and tuneless, like wolf howls.
iii) The audience were eating raw meat and were very hairy.

Simile of the Day
A monkey's as much use to a vacuum cleaner as a vacuum cleaner is to a monkey.

Q3 Is the description in Q2 a simile or a metaphor?

Q4 Copy and complete the table showing the similes and metaphors that the writer uses.

Thing being described	Description the writer uses	Simile or metaphor	What this means
Leo Ryder			
Arnie X playing guitar			
Jay Bryson beating the drums			

Hello, I'm three — I've never metaphor before...

Fictional writing uses shiploads of metaphors and similes. They're imported from Greece, though some arrive on the black market to avoid customs tax. Learn to spot 'em. Also learn to spot bull.

Mood

Fiction writers build up the mood of a scene through the language they use. Basically, mood is about how the text makes you feel — whether it's happy, sad, funny, frightening, exciting...

A At last the waiting was over. Rachel held the exam results envelope and watched her friends opening theirs. Some smiled with relief, some stared at the floor.

Her fingers tugged gently at the envelope.

Slightly open now...

Nearly there...

B The mood took hold of the family like a virus. Mealtimes were now a matter of muttered greetings, lowered eyes and shared silences. Even the cracked ceilings had begun to weep rainwater. Gordon knew that Dexter had been *only* a dog, but he was missed like a member of the family.

C Katie strolled amid the laughing guests, her son Daniel trotting at her side. The sun caressed Katie's skin, while a cool breeze tickled the hair falling on her neck. The grass beneath her feet provided a soft carpet. Katie hadn't felt so alive in years.

Q1 Match up each of the texts A, B and C to one of the moods below.

tense romantic happy horrific funny sad

Q2 In text A, is Rachel in a hurry to open the envelope? Use evidence from the extract to back up your answer.

Q3 Why do you think the writer of text B used the word "weep" instead of "let in"? Mention the overall mood of the text in your answer.

Q4 What does the word 'trotting' in text C tell you about how Daniel feels?

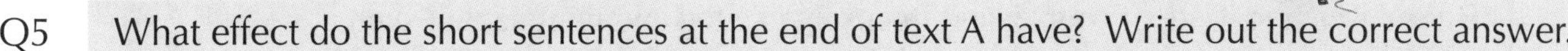

Q5 What effect do the short sentences at the end of text A have? Write out the correct answer.

i) They slow the pace down before Rachel opens the envelope, which builds up suspense.

ii) They speed the pace up after Rachel opens the envelope, which builds up suspense.

Q6 Which of the three texts would the sentence below fit into? Write a sentence to explain your answer.

Even in crowds people kept a respectful distance, turning their long, pale faces away.

Q7 Write a couple of sentences explaining what the phrase "muttered greetings, lowered eyes and shared silences" from text B tells you about the mood of the text.

Long Language Question

Time to try your hand at dealing with a longer text — the texts in the SATs will be at least 1 page long. Read the extract below and then have a go at answering the questions opposite.

This is an extract from the short story *The Sea Raiders* by H.G. Wells.

Mr Fison, torn by curiosity, began picking his way across the wave-worn rocks, and, finding the wet seaweed that covered them thickly rendered* them extremely slippery, he stopped, removed his shoes and socks, and coiled his trousers above his knees. His object was, of course, merely to avoid stumbling into the rocky pools about him, and perhaps he was rather glad, as all men are, of an excuse to resume, even for a moment, the sensations of his boyhood. At any rate, it is to this, no doubt, that he owes his life.

He approached his mark with all the assurance which the absolute security of this country against all forms of animal life gives its inhabitants. The round bodies moved to and fro, but it was only when he surmounted the skerry* of boulders I have mentioned that he realised the horrible nature of the discovery. It came upon him with some suddenness.

The rounded bodies fell apart as he came into sight over the ridge, and displayed the pinkish object to be the partially devoured body of a human being, but whether of a man or woman he was unable to say. And the rounded bodies were new and ghastly looking creatures, in shape somewhat resembling an octopus, and with huge and very long and flexible tentacles, coiled copiously on the ground. The skin had a glistening texture, unpleasant to see, like shiny leather. The downward bend of the tentacle-surrounded mouth, the curious excrescence* at the bend, the tentacles, and the large intelligent eyes, gave the creatures a grotesque suggestion of a face. They were the size of a fair-sized swine about the body, and the tentacles seemed to him to be many feet in length. There were, he thinks, seven or eight at least of the creatures. Twenty yards beyond them, amid the surf of the now returning tide, two others were emerging from the sea.

Their bodies lay flatly on the rocks, and their eyes regarded him with evil interest; but it does not appear that Mr Fison was afraid, or that he realised that he was in any danger. Possibly his confidence is to be ascribed to the limpness of their attitudes. But he was horrified, of course, and intensely excited and indignant at such revolting creatures preying upon human flesh. He thought they had chanced upon a drowned body. He shouted to them, with the idea of driving them off, and, finding they did not budge, cast about him, picked up a big rounded lump of rock, and flung it at one.

And then, slowly uncoiling their tentacles, they all began moving towards him — creeping at first deliberately, and making a soft purring sound to each other.

rendered = *made*
skerry = *mound*
excrescence = *growth*

Long Language Question

OK, so maybe 'The Sea Raiders' is gruesome and bloodthirsty, but it's also chock-full of descriptions and other tricks that all good writers use. Answer these questions about it.

Q1 Read the third paragraph carefully and write out any phrases that describe what the creatures look like.

Q2 Quickly sketch a picture of one of the creatures, using descriptions from the third paragraph.

Q3 Write down which of the following words from the text are adjectives and which are adverbs.

i) wave-worn ii) horrible iii) ghastly iv) copiously v) flexible
vi) glistening vii) flatly viii) intensely ix) revolting x) slowly

Not sure what adjectives and adverbs are? Look them up and write out the definitions.

Q4 Which of the following extracts from the text contains a simile? Copy out the correct answer.

i) And the rounded bodies were new and ghastly looking creatures...
ii) The skin had a glistening texture, unpleasant to see, like shiny leather.
iii) Their bodies lay flatly on the rocks, and their eyes regarded him with evil interest...
iv) They were the size of a fair-sized swine...

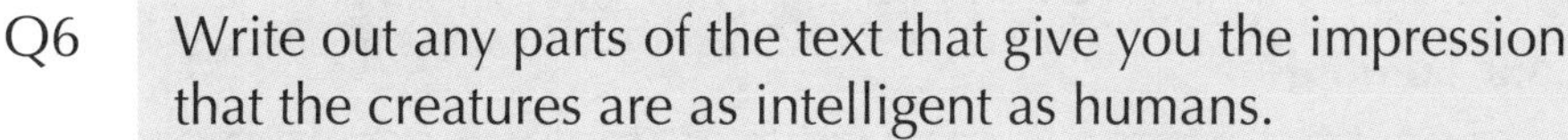

Q5 Write out any words from the fourth paragraph of the extract that tell you about Mr Fison's reaction to the creatures.

Q6 Write out any parts of the text that give you the impression that the creatures are as intelligent as humans.

Q7 Write out any parts of the text that tell you about how the creatures move.

Q8 Which row of the table sums up how the creatures move and what effect the movement achieves?

	How the creatures move	Effect this achieves
i)	Very slowly	Makes the reader feel sad
ii)	Very quickly	Makes the text funnier
iii)	Very slowly	Builds up suspense
iv)	Very quickly	Builds up suspense

Q9 In the extract from *The Sea Raiders*, how does the writer convey the horror of the situation to the reader? Write half a page, using the questions on this page as prompts. (10 marks)

Convey the horror — eat the reader's face off...

Don't read the text just once — keep looking back at it when you're doing the questions. Pick out the bit of the text that the question refers to, and then read that bit again carefully.

Layout

Some of the texts that you get in the SATs will be laid out in a special way, e.g. with bullet points, headings or arrows. There are often questions about how the layout makes the information clearer. Look at the following three extracts and answer all the questions at the bottom of the page.

A

Tues 3rd Feb — Video camera finally arrived! Can't believe it took three weeks to get here.

Wed 4th Feb — Been playing with camera all day. Caroline came round and we wrote and filmed a pretend TV show. I got to be a game show host (naturally).

Thu 5th Feb — Dropped camera when I was trying to film myself on a skateboard — it doesn't look too healthy any more. Think I might take up photography instead.

B

<u>Why go to the Lake District?</u> It may not be the most 'happening' place, but there are often locally produced performances in Kendal, or specialist art films showing at the cinema.

<u>What's in the local area?</u> Well, most people go to the Lake District to walk in the hills. If you're less of an outdoor type, there are plenty of other diversions. The 'Theatre by the Lake' in Keswick is well worth a look.

<u>Does anyone care about the Lake District?</u>
The Royal Shakespeare Company regularly tour Keswick and Kendal. The arts centre in Kendal is a member of the British Film Institute, so it often shows restored classic films.

C

Five tips for a healthy computer:

1. **Always shut down the computer correctly after use.**
2. **Try not to have more than three applications running at once.** → Using lots of programs at once will slow your computer down.
3. **Always scan discs for viruses before you use them.** → See next page for more on viruses.
4. **Make sure your computer base unit is well ventilated.** → Don't block the fan at the back of the unit, or it will overheat.
5. **Don't eat or drink near your computer.**

Q1 What kind of text do you think Extract A is taken from? Explain your answer.

Q2 Explain why it's important that the writer of Extract A included dates as subheadings.

Q3 Why are the subheadings in Extract B written as questions? Write out the best answer.

i) To make the article feel like a speech read out by the writer.

ii) To make the article feel like a conversation between the writer and the reader.

iii) To annoy the reader and to make them feel stupid.

Q4 Why has the writer of Extract C numbered the five points?

Q5 Explain the purpose of the information in grey boxes in Extract C.

Q6 How do the arrows in Extract C help the reader to understand the text?

Structure

As well as layout, writers have to think about the order they put their information. You can get questions about this in the SATs, e.g. what makes a good introduction or conclusion.

A book review for a popular magazine

If asked about writer Alexis Bright, most people would react: "Who?" However, all this is about to change...

Bright's new novel, 'A Tale of Two Celebrities', is a vicious attack on the nature of celebrity in the 21st century. Set in present-day Manchester, it tells the story of the rivalry between failing TV host Richard and rising star Penelope.

The novel's fans (and there will be many) will applaud the author's bold statements and the unflinching satire of our obsession with celebrities. The book is sure to do brisk business, and is likely to be a big seller in airports and newsagents.

On the other hand, many people will scoff at the two-dimensional characters, as well as the unsatisfying ending (in which Richard and Penelope fight it out on air in a duel-like ratings war).

So, next time someone asks you about Alexis Bright, you'd better have read 'A Tale of Two Celebrities', so that you know where you stand.

Q1 Explain one way in which the first paragraph is effective as an introduction to the article.

Q2 Write a sentence to sum up what the writer tells you in the second paragraph.

Q3 Why do you think the writer put that paragraph straight after the introduction?

Q4 Sum up the differences between paragraphs 3 and 4, in one sentence.

Q5 Why do you think the writer put paragraphs 3 and 4 next to each other?

Q6 Write out the answer below that explains why the last sentence is a good ending to the text.

i) The last sentence refers back to the introduction and sums up the main point of the review.

ii) The last sentence makes a new point that is better than the other points in the text.

iii) The last sentence tries to persuade the reader that 'A Tale of Two Celebrities' is terrible.

Q7 SAT-STYLE QUESTION Explain how the writer structures the book review in a way that keeps the reader interested. Write about half a page and use your answers to the above questions to help you.

(10 marks)

Structure — point don't I it of see the...

Writing needs to be well structured in order to get information across to the reader in a clear and logical way. The examiners think this is as important as regular teeth-brushing, so pay attention.

Persuading the Reader

Sometimes writers try to change the way the reader feels about something, whether it's in fiction or non-fiction. You need to know how to describe the tricks writers use to persuade you.

Questions 1 and 2 are about the advert for Bonza Biscuits below.

NEW! *Bonza Biscuits!*

Bonza Biscuits **are the new luxury biscuit treat from Butler's Biscuit company. Not only are they tasty, they're great value too.**

Special introductory offer — only 70p per pack!

Hurry to your local supermarket or Butler's Biscuits seller and demand your first packet of *Bonza Biscuits*. Introductory offer lasts 2 weeks only.
Bonza Biscuits **— the most satisfying chocolate biscuits you'll ever have.**

Q1 What is the main aim of the advert?

Q2 Pick out all the phrases from the text that try to persuade the reader that Bonza Biscuits are great.

Watch out for words that exaggerate how wonderful the biscuits are.

Questions 3–5 are about the extract below.

Looking at Mr Blister's face was like looking at a wet sponge wearing a hat. His narrow eyes squinted through his finger-printed spectacles, as if even looking at the idiots around him made him feel ill. He would often raise his pudgy, clay-like hand to rub his peeling nose or to wipe his damp forehead.

Mr Blister bellowed instead of talking and he walked like a toad, moving in jumps and starts, taking long strides with his tree-trunk legs.

Q3 Copy out and fill in this table showing the descriptions of Mr Blister's body parts.

Body part	Description
legs	like tree trunks
forehead	
hands	
eyes	
nose	

You can just copy out the descriptions from the text for this question.

Q4 Write out the answer that is the best short description of Mr Blister.

i) Mr Blister is a decent, good-looking man.

ii) Mr Blister is ugly but he's basically a nice person.

iii) Mr Blister is a really ugly and unpleasant man.

Q5 Write a short passage explaining whether or not you think the writer wants the reader to like Mr Blister. Use your answers to Q3 and Q4 to help you. (3 marks)

SAT-STYLE QUESTION

Changes in the Writer's Opinion

Examiners love it if you spot when a writer's opinion changes during a text. So make the SATs examiners as happy as mice in a vat of cheese, and have a go at these questions.

Extract from an article called *All The Fun of the Fair?*

Ever since I've been very young I've been taken to circuses around the world. My parents saw it as an educational experience — and there was also the fact that I would get ridiculously excited at the sight of the animals on display. Lions, elephants, trained horses — all these animals prompted the same breathless response from me.

In the years since then I've always retained a fondness for circuses despite the recent bad press — so naturally I was delighted to accept an offer to go backstage at Jackson's Travelling Circus.

Unfortunately, the reality of the circus was far less exotic than I had previously believed. The lions in their cramped cages hardly resembled the proud hunters I'd imagined. The sight of the elephants pacing sadly up and down brought tears to my eyes. Even the beaming grins of the human performers were discarded once they'd left the ring.

Q1 Which of these phrases from the article does not show the writer's view of circuses as a child?

i) My parents saw it as an educational experience

ii) I would get ridiculously excited at the sight of the animals on display

iii) all these animals prompted the same breathless response from me

Q2 What happened to change the writer's opinion of circuses?

FREEDOM

Q3 In which paragraph does the tone of the article become negative?

Q4 Write out a phrase from the text that signals this change of focus.

Q5 Write out a phrase from the text that shows the writer's emotions during the backstage tour.

Q6 Why did the writer add a question mark to the title of the article?
Explain why the answer below is wrong, and write out a better answer.

The writer added a question mark to the title 'All The Fun of the Fair?' to show that she used to believe that circuses were boring, but now she thinks that they're really exciting.

Q7 SAT-STYLE QUESTION Write a short paragraph explaining why the writer's opinion changes during the extract. Use your answers to the questions on this page to help you. (5 marks)

Great page — no it's not — yes it is...

Writers often give clues about their opinions in non-fiction texts — and mentioning if their opinions change will definitely get you buckets of extra marks. Which is better than a poke in the eye.

The Effect on the Reader

**Writers try hard to get the reader involved in the story or argument.
You've got to keep your eyes peeled for ways that the reader will be affected by the text.**

An extract from the book *I was a Member of the Barrow Gang*

> OK, just imagine the situation: an open safe, piles and piles of shining golden coins just waiting for me to get my hands on them — and surely you don't think I was unreasonable in assuming that my partners-in-crime had all been caught by now...
>
> I don't believe that there's a person in this world who would've done the decent thing and given themselves up to the police. Sure, I could have gone outside and tried to help out my partners, but you and I know that there would have been no point.
>
> Well, of course I took the money and ran. Wouldn't you?

Q1 Write a couple of sentences describing who the narrator is and what's happened.

Q2 Write out the phrase in the text that contains a rhetorical question.

Rhetorical questions are questions that don't need an answer.

Q3 What effect does the rhetorical question have on the reader? Write out the best answer.

i) It sounds as if the character is talking to himself.

ii) It sounds as if the character is talking to you and it involves you in the decision.

iii) It sounds as if the reader is asking the main character a question.

Q4 Write out the sentence below that explains why the writer chooses to include the phrase 'imagine the situation'.

i) The writer wants the reader to be the main character in the story.

ii) The writer wants to stop the reader from identifying with the main character.

iii) The writer wants to make the reader feel like they're actually taking part in the story.

Q5 Which of these phrases directly involves the reader in the story? Write out the correct phrases.

piles and piles of shining golden coins	you and I know that there would have been no point	of course I took the money and ran	surely you don't think I was unreasonable

Q6 SAT-STYLE QUESTION How does the writer involve the reader in the story?
Use your answers to the questions on this page to help you. (5 marks)

Check for split sides and wet pants...

Always show the examiner that you understand what the writing is trying to do. Even if you don't find something funny, it's worth saying if you think something is <u>supposed</u> to be funny.

Comparing Texts

Questions that ask you to compare different texts are sure to come up in the SATs. Read through each of these texts, then turn the page and have a go at answering the questions.

A scientific account called *The Macaque Monkeys of Japan*

Day 1 — Macaque monkeys currently living in the centre of the island, within the forest area. Monkeys' day-to-day activities seem to be entirely according to accepted theories. Diet seems to be largely composed of berries.

Day 2 — Team placed large amount of potatoes in forest. May have to wait a while to see if the macaques show any interest.

Day 6 — It worked! Two days ago, the monkeys showed some interest in the potatoes — and since then they have made potatoes the main part of their diet. Team intends to move piles of potatoes closer to shore to see if the macaques follow.

Day 9 — Macaques definitely becoming comfortable with living on shoreline now, entirely depending on potatoes we supply. I even saw one monkey washing a potato in the sea before eating it! This development entirely unprecedented — seems to prove that monkeys are capable of dramatically changing their living patterns.

Day 11 — Macaques now entirely at home by shoreline. A few making effort to learn to swim in sea, and others starting to copy. Experiment declared a success — the macaques are learning afresh how to live their day-to-day life.

Monkeys of the World Unite! You have Nothing to Lose but your Bananas

An extract from the novel *I, Monkey*

This is getting ridiculous. It was just a bit of fun letting the humans teach me sign language (and it really wasn't hard to learn) — but now they're excited and buzzing around like annoying flies. They've started saying that I'm the first ape to show real intelligence — the cheek of it! Just because we don't usually choose to humour their dreary experiments doesn't mean that we aren't capable of getting a message across.

Lots of people have come to visit since I started answering back through sign language. Most of them are pretty sad specimens with faces as pale as their white coats. I was going to give them a nice surprise by saying a few words, maybe have a chat about the weather — but it's getting boring now, so I think I might just be on my way.

instinct = in-built patterns of behaviour in response to certain things

An extract from an article called *Monkey Behaviour*

Humans may learn a lot from insects and animals. Humans will always question what they're doing and why they're doing it — but, for instance, a worker bee will always know its role in the beehive. It may feed the young or guard the hive, but it will always carry out its duty without even needing to be told. The same is true of more 'intelligent' organisms, such as the monkey. Although monkeys can be taught tricks (even to the extent of appearing to relish drinking tea in TV adverts), they are not able to break out of the simple instinctive pattern which instructs them exactly how to live their lives.

Too right.
Down with this
sort of thing.

Comparing Texts

Keep turning the page to check the texts when you're doing these questions. In the SATs you'll probably only have to compare two texts, but I've given you three for extra practice.

Q1 Match up each text to its description.

The Macaque Monkeys of Japan	Story
I, Monkey	Magazine article
Monkey Behaviour	Diary

Q2 Write out a phrase from *I, Monkey* that contains a simile.

Q3 Write out a phrase from *I, Monkey* that uses humour.

Q4 Write out a sentence from *The Macaque Monkeys of Japan* that is written in informal language.

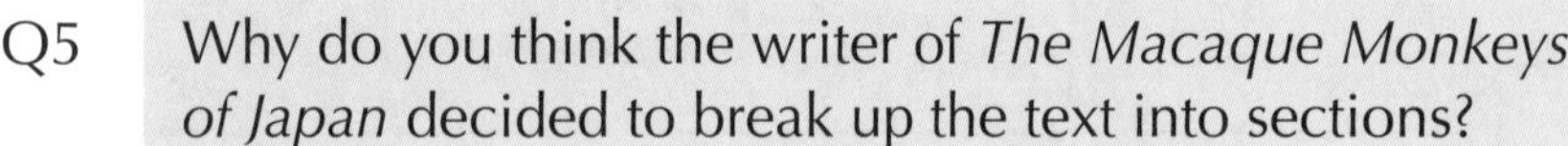

Q5 Why do you think the writer of *The Macaque Monkeys of Japan* decided to break up the text into sections?

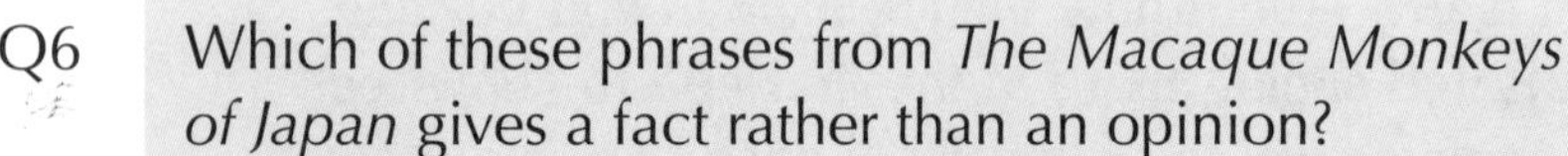

Q6 Which of these phrases from *The Macaque Monkeys of Japan* gives a fact rather than an opinion?

i) Macaque monkeys currently living in the centre of the island

ii) seems to prove that monkeys are capable of dramatically changing their living patterns

iii) the macaques are learning afresh how to live their day-to-day life

Q7 Write out the paragraph that sums up what happens in the extract from *I, Monkey*.

i) The scientists believe that monkeys are only capable of learning very basic sign language. The scientists are clever, so they are probably right.

ii) The monkey is more intelligent than the scientists realise. The monkey tells the story from his point of view, which shows the scientists are wrong.

Q8 Write out the paragraph that sums up the writer's opinion in *Monkey Behaviour*.

i) The writer thinks that humans are not ruled by instinct, but that all animals and insects are.

ii) The writer thinks that humans are ruled by instinct, but animals and insects are not.

iii) The writer thinks that all animals, including humans, are completely ruled by instinct.

Comparing Texts

Now you can move on to the longer comparing questions. When you're comparing two texts, make sure you don't write too much on one — write an equal amount for each text.

Q9 Write out the sentence that best describes the main idea in all three texts.

i) All three texts are about whether monkeys can instinctively talk.

ii) All three texts are about whether the behaviour of monkeys is purely instinctive.

iii) All three texts are about whether monkeys know that their behaviour is instinctive.

Q10 Copy and complete this table comparing all three texts.
Use your answers to the questions on the previous page to help you.

Name of extract	The Macaque Monkeys of Japan	I, Monkey	Monkey Behaviour
Is the extract fiction or non-fiction?			
Is descriptive language used?			
Is the language formal or informal?			
Is there a first-person narrator?			
Does the writer use facts to back up their points?			
Does the writer think that animals are ruled by instinct?			

Now make use of your answers so far to answer the next three questions.
The table above is going to be especially useful.

Q11 SAT-STYLE QUESTION Re-read *The Macaque Monkeys of Japan* and *I, Monkey*. Write a short description of the differences between the layout and structure of each of the texts. (3 marks)

Q12 SAT-STYLE QUESTION Re-read *I, Monkey* and *Monkey Behaviour*. Write a paragraph describing the differences between the language used in each of the texts. (3 marks)

Q13 SAT-STYLE QUESTION Re-read *The Macaque Monkeys of Japan* and *Monkey Behaviour*. Write a paragraph describing the differences between the writers' opinions about animal instinct. (3 marks)

"Romeo & Julie" — "do I get my banana now?" ***(monkey 5882)***

Questions 11-13 on this page are like the ones you'll get in the SATs. Don't forget that you should write the same amount on both of the texts you're comparing, if you want to get good marks.

Answers Without Prompts

Sometimes those mean SATs examiners give you questions without any hints at all. You should always write out a list of prompts to remind you of the things you need to mention in your answer. When you've read the text on the flap have a go at these questions.

Q1 Here's a question with no prompts at all. Copy out and correct the answer to the question.

Explain how Oscar Wilde's use of similes and metaphors conveys Dorian's state of mind in the extract.

Hint: There are two errors in the answer.

Wilde writes that "a sharp pang of pain struck like a knife across him", and this metaphor shows that Dorian feels physically hurt when he realises that he will grow old. Later, Dorian calms down again when Wilde writes that "he felt as if a hand of ice had been laid upon his heart".

Q2 Write out the group of three prompts that would help you to answer the question below.

Comment on the way that Lord Henry and Basil Hallward act towards Dorian Gray.

- *How does Hallward feel about Lord Henry?*
- *How does Lord Henry react to Hallward?*
- *How does Dorian feel about the painting?*

- *How does Hallward feel about his painting?*
- *How does Lord Henry react to seeing the painting?*
- *What do the characters say to Dorian before and after seeing the painting?*

Q3 Explain why the group of three prompts that you didn't pick would be unsuitable.

Q4 Write out three of the prompts in grey boxes that would help you answer the question below.

Comment on the effectiveness of the language used to describe old age in the extract.

- *How does the language make the reader feel about old age?*
- *What does panegyric mean?*
- *What is Lord Henry's opinion about old age?*
- *What happens to make Dorian change his opinion of old age?*
- *Which phrases describe Dorian's body when he is old?*
- *Does Oscar Wilde use similes and metaphors in the extract?*

Q5 Write a list of three prompts that would help you answer the question below.

What is Dorian Gray's opinion of old age by the end of the extract?

Answers Without Prompts

The two pages of questions are about breaking long questions down into smaller pieces. Read the extract below and then have a go at the questions, referring back whenever you need to.

This is an extract from the novel *The Picture of Dorian Gray* by Oscar Wilde.

After about a quarter of an hour, Hallward stopped painting, looked for a long time at Dorian Gray, and then for a long time at the picture, biting the end of one of his huge brushes, and smiling. "It is quite finished," he cried, at last, and stooping down he wrote his name in thin vermilion letters on the left-hand corner of the canvas.

Lord Henry came over and examined the picture. It was certainly a wonderful work of art, and a wonderful likeness as well.

"My dear fellow, I congratulate you most warmly," he said.—"Mr. Gray, come and look at yourself."

The lad started, as if awakened from some dream. "Is it really finished?" he murmured, stepping down from the platform.

"Quite finished," said Hallward. "And you have sat splendidly to-day. I am awfully obliged to you."

"That is entirely due to me," broke in Lord Henry. "Isn't it, Mr. Gray?"

Dorian made no answer, but passed listlessly in front of his picture and turned towards it. When he saw it he drew back, and his cheeks flushed for a moment with pleasure. A look of joy came into his eyes, as if he had recognized himself for the first time. He stood there motionless, and in wonder, dimly conscious that Hallward was speaking to him, but not catching the meaning of his words. The sense of his own beauty came on him like a revelation. He had never felt it before. Basil Hallward's compliments had seemed to him to be merely the charming exaggerations of friendship. He had listened to them, laughed at them, forgotten them. They had not influenced his nature. Then had come Lord Henry, with his strange panegyric on youth, his terrible warning of its brevity. That had stirred him at the time, and now, as he stood gazing at the shadow of his own loveliness, the full reality of the description flashed across him. Yes, there would be a day when his face would be wrinkled and wizen, his eyes dim and colourless, the grace of his figure broken and deformed. The scarlet would pass away from his lips, and the gold steal from his hair. The life that was to make his soul would mar his body. He would become ignoble, hideous, and uncouth.

As he thought of it, a sharp pang of pain struck like a knife across him, and made each delicate fibre of his nature quiver. His eyes deepened into amethyst, and a mist of tears came across them.

He felt as if a hand of ice had been laid upon his heart.

"Don't you like it?" cried Hallward at last, stung a little by the lad's silence, and not understanding what it meant.

"Of course he likes it," said Lord Henry. "Who wouldn't like it? It is one of the greatest things in modern art. I will give you anything you like to ask for it. I must have it."

"It is not my property, Harry."

"Whose property is it?"

"Dorian's, of course."

"He is a very lucky fellow."

"How sad it is!" murmured Dorian Gray, with his eyes still fixed upon his own portrait. "How sad it is! I shall grow old, and horrid, and dreadful. But this picture will remain always young. It will never be older than this particular day of June. . . . If it was only the other way! If it was I who were to be always young, and the picture that were to grow old! For this—for this—I would give everything! Yes, there is nothing in the whole world I would not give!"

panegyric = a speech in praise of something

FOLD THIS PAGE OUT

Read the text, then do the questions on the following pages.

Answers Without Prompts

Another page about how to deal with long, murderous questions which give you no hints at all. [N.B. You can also try leaving the country and buying a house in Rio.]

Q6 Write out the sentence that sums up Dorian's view of himself at the start of the extract.

i) Dorian isn't really aware of his beauty and doesn't believe the nice things that people say.

ii) Dorian knows he is beautiful and loves hearing people say nice things about him.

iii) Dorian is vain and wants everyone to see his beautiful portrait.

Q7 Copy out phrases from the text that back up your answer to Q6.

Q8 What happens in the text to make Dorian change his opinion of himself?

Q9 How does Dorian feel about his appearance afterwards? Write out the correct answer.

i) Dorian realises that he is not as beautiful as he thought beforehand.

ii) Dorian realises that he is as beautiful as people have been telling him.

iii) Dorian wishes that he was even more beautiful that he already is.

Q10 Copy out a phrase from the text that backs up your answer to Q9.

Q11 How does Dorian feel about growing old? Copy and correct this answer.

Hint: There are two errors in the answer.

Dorian imagines when his face is 'wrinkled and wizen' and he feels so horrified that the thought hurts 'like a sword across him'. He imagines when 'the scarlet would pass away from his lips', which shows that he thinks that he will become mean as well as ugly.

Q12 What does Dorian wish for at the end of the extract? What does this tell you about his feelings?

Q13 Use questions 6-12 to write a list of prompts to answer the question at the bottom of the page.

Q14 Now answer this SAT-style question. Your prompts and answers from all the other questions on this page should help loads.

SAT-STYLE QUESTION

How does Dorian Gray's opinion of himself change during the extract?	(5 marks)

Born to be Wilde...

Phew... now you've done these pages you'll be able to break down long questions into manageable chunks, bung them on cocktail sticks and eat 'em like pineapple.

Proper SAT Reading Questions

SAT-STYLE QUESTIONS

Now it's high time that you put all the skills together to tackle some real(ish) SATs questions. When you've read the article on the left have a go at these short questions.

Q1 Which country hosted the first World Cup? (1 mark)

Q2 Copy and complete the table below showing facts from the extract. (3 marks)

Description of fact	Number
Year of first World Cup final	
Largest stadium audience	
Year Football Association was created	
Total viewing figures of 1998 World Cup	
Year Charles Miller took football to Brazil	
Number of teams playing in first World Cup Final	
Year World Cup match sparked a war	

Q3 Write down the first country to play football on record, and how long ago that was. (1 mark)

Q4 Write down the two countries involved in a war sparked off by a World Cup match. (1 mark)

Q5 Who originally thought up the idea of the World Cup? (1 mark)

Q6 Where was the World Cup created? (1 mark)

Q7 Why do you think the writer says that "the history of football goes back ever so slightly further than 1930"? (2 marks)

Q8 Why do you think the writer used the phrase "snarling like hyenas" to describe the football fans in the first paragraph? (2 marks)

Q9 Why do you think the writer uses the phrase "bloody, sweaty battlefield" at the end of the third paragraph? (2 marks)

Q10 Explain why the writer numbered the points in the section "What's so great about football?". (2 marks)

Q11 Why do you think the writer uses questions for the subheadings? (2 marks)

KEEP TURNING

Proper SAT Reading Questions

You know the drill — read the text carefully, have a go at the questions, refer back to this text whenever you need to. Except this time there are loads more questions, and they're trickier too.

This is an extract from a magazine article called *World Cup Fever*.

A shrill blast. The 'thunk' of leather against leather. The air is filled with the sounds of shouting and stamping feet. Thousands of people with brightly painted faces are snarling like hyenas at their opponents. No, this is not a scene from the film *Braveheart*. It's even more serious — it's the World Cup.

The World Cup was thought up by Jules Rimet in Paris, and the first Final was in 1930. The host, Uruguay, offered to pay for travel expenses for the other teams. They were rewarded by winning, and declared a national day of holiday. Mind you, there were only 13 teams playing!

Where did football come from?

The history of football goes back ever so slightly further than 1930. The first records of the game were about 5000 years ago in China. Versions of football were also played by the ancient Greeks, Egyptians, and Romans. In the 16th century in Italy, a similar game called *calcio* was played, with a decapitated head used for the ball! In Britain we weren't much more humane either. Imagine the scene in medieval England: it's a national holiday and virtually every town in the country is turned into a bloody, sweaty battlefield that only faintly resembles a football pitch.

Later on, the British claimed the game as their own, before introducing it to countries around the world. In 1894 Charles Miller changed the face of Brazil for good when he left his boat carrying a football in each hand. Now most people recognise Brazil as the home of the most beautifully played football in the world.

The modern rules of football were only made concrete in 1963 when the Football Association was founded – and the game has evolved into the one we know and love today.

Is it *really* the beautiful game?

So, the modern game of football has inspired and entertained people for decades, but it hasn't all been good. We're all aware of the phenomenon of football hooliganism. Although more and more regulations are being brought in to prevent them, these idiots continue to spoil the game for many other people. However, football has been indirectly responsible for even worse things. In 1969 a controversial World Cup qualifying match between El Salvador and Honduras contributed to war breaking out between the two countries!

Proper SAT Reading Questions

What's so great about football?

Football is amazingly popular around the world. The largest stadium audience for a game was in Rio de Janeiro for the 1950 World Cup Final, when 200,000 people turned up to see the game. Nowadays, matches are transmitted live to the whole world on TV. The total viewing figures for the whole of the 1998 World Cup were 33.4 billion people from 196 countries — and there's only 6 billion people in the world, so everyone must have watched lots of different matches!

There are many ideas about why football is so popular around the world:

1) *The basic rules are very simple – they don't need much explanation and so people can play football without even being able to talk the same language.*
2) *It doesn't take much organisation – all you need is a ball, a flat space of land and some markers for goalposts.*
3) *There's the potential for real drama – the game is very physical, and footballers can show off their skills.*

Who are the biggest football fans?

During World Cup season in Brazil, walls and lampposts are often painted in the national team colours of green and yellow. In Britain we might not be quite as dramatic, but in 2002 we once again proved our devotion to football when thousands of people made excuses to miss school or work in order to watch the World Cup games held in South Korea and Japan. Even those of us who wouldn't normally watch football managed to get caught up in the national excitement, including me...

...but I still don't understand the offside rule.

FOLD THIS PAGE OUT

Read the text, then do the questions on the following pages.

SAT-STYLE QUESTIONS

Proper SAT Reading Questions

Thinking that the last page was a bit of a doddle? This one's full of longer SAT-style questions. Remember that it's often useful to break long questions down into smaller chunks.

Q12 Explain one way in which the first paragraph is effective as an introduction to the article. Use phrases from the text to back up your answer. (3 marks)

Q13 Copy and complete the table, by summing up each subsection in one sentence. (3 marks)

Subsection	Summary
Introduction	
'Where did football come from?'	
'Is it really the beautiful game?'	
'What's so great about football?'	
'Who are the biggest football fans?'	

Q14 Sum up the whole article in no more than three sentences. (2 marks)

Q15 The section "Is it *really* the beautiful game?" is more negative than the rest of the text. Write out one phrase from this section that tells you the writer's opinion. (2 marks)

Q16 Explain what Charles Miller did to "change the face of Brazil". (2 marks)

Q17 The article begins: "A shrill blast. The 'thunk' of leather against leather." Explain what the writer is referring to in these two sentences. (2 marks)

Q18 Using facts from the text, give three reasons why football is extremely popular. (2 marks)

Q19 Do you think the final sentence is a good ending to the text? Back up your answer with phrases from the text. (5 marks)

Q20 Sum up the writer's opinion of football, using evidence from the whole text to back up your answer. (5 marks)

Q21 How does the writer use humour to keep the reader interested? Use phrases from the text to back up your answer. (5 marks)

Q22 In the whole article, explain how the writer presents the history of football as both positive and surprisingly violent. (5 marks)

Stressful And Tiring *(anonymous quote)*

In the SAT there'll be about five questions per text. I've given you millions of questions about the text because I'm just generous with giving you practice. If I say so myself. Oh, now I'm blushing.

Sentences, Phrases and Clauses

Use language correctly and the SAT examiners will reward you with a pile of juicy marks. Grammar's here to haunt you until the end of your days — so get it sorted.

Q1 Read parts a)-i). Write down why each one isn't a proper sentence.

a) The dog walked slowly up the drive, regretting the mess he'd made of the roses
b) the wind in my hair.
c) Paul said that he liked Vienna
d) The Romans' legendary cruelty to Octavia.
e) Wanted a headlamp for his car.
f) she wants to go but her father thinks it's a silly idea
g) Before the winter.
h) Ran to the shops.
i) Bananas for £2.20 a kilo.

Psst — you ain't seen me, right?

Q2 Write down whether a)-i) are phrases, clauses or main clauses.

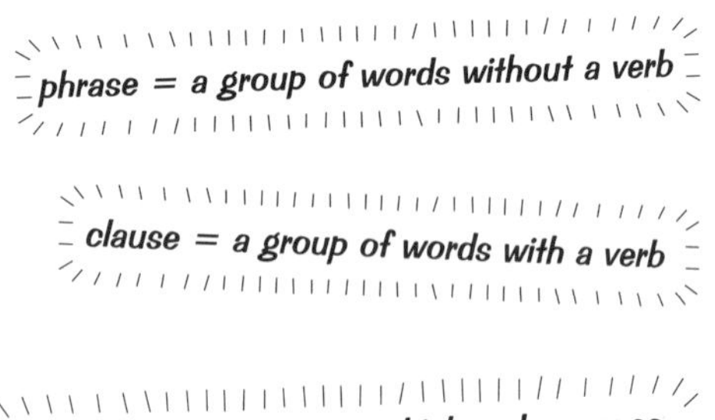

phrase = a group of words without a verb
clause = a group of words with a verb
main clause = a clause which makes sense on its own and could be a sentence

a) the hedgehog's evil spikes
b) spitting in the fish tank
c) we went to Olivia Newton-John's house
d) running to the river
e) on the way to the bus
f) Rita Hayworth is gorgeous
g) in the autumn
h) William paused thoughtfully
i) despite the heavy rain

verb = a 'doing' or 'being' word

Q3 Match up the phrases and the clauses below. Write them out as sentences, putting a comma between the phrase and the clause.

Phrases

a) Before the start of term
b) In the Atlantic ocean
c) In his best Western movies
d) Without a bit of mustard
e) Without a doubt
f) Very well then
g) In a desperate attempt at humour
h) Up in the attic

Clauses

1) you can see fish swimming
2) this recipe tastes disgusting
3) my brother tried to poison a rat
4) porridge is better than gruel
5) I'll fight you for it
6) Gary Cooper's acting was impressive
7) Kim threw the egg against the wall
8) I'll have to cram in lots of fun

Commas, Semicolons and Colons

Commas, semi-colons and colons are all used to break sentences up into manageable chunks. Try pausing slightly where you want to put the comma, etc. to see if it sounds right.

Q1 Copy out the following sentences, adding commas, to make the meaning clearer.

a) Walking beside the miniature poodle Harley felt very tall indeed.

b) Helen pitied the spider in the sink which was about to die.

c) Scurrying out of the way of the headmistress Dana looked a bit sheepish.

d) He walked and talked half an hour afterwards his head was cut off.

Q2 Copy out the sentences, adding commas to separate the clauses and phrases.

e.g. Though a good singer Frank Sinatra was a naughty man in real life.
Though a good singer, Frank Sinatra was a naughty man in real life.

phrase

clause

a) After the storm was over my sister returned to the ranch.

b) Despite everything I still had a soft spot for her.

c) He marched away from the station without a single look back.

d) Way back many centuries ago not long after the Bible began Jacob lived in the land of Canaan a fine example of a family man.

e) Although the weather was hot Abigail decided to wear a big jumper and corduroy trousers.

Q3 All these sentences have colons missing.
Copy out the sentences, adding colons in the right place.

Colons are used: 1) before lists, 2) before a long quotation, 3) before an explanation.

a) I'll tell you how I managed it I walked up to him and asked him.

b) All I want from my hamster is companionship, devotion and a small but tasty meal.

c) As my grandmother says "Don't fight with your Grandad or I'll get you."

d) You should bring the following things an inflatable dinghy, a life jacket and a foghorn.

e) Pigeons have been known to communicate as follows "eeuak, eak, ouawk, ek-ek, ooch."

Q4 The following sentences have semicolons in the wrong place.
Copy out the sentences, moving the semicolons to the right places.

a) The star required: a trailer with a jacuzzi three servants; including a manicurist a separate dog kennel and; Scottish salmon sandwiches without crusts.

b) The footballer had it all: a strong left foot a good eye; for the ball a lightning pace; and nerves of steel.

Semi-colons are used to join together linked sentences, and to break up lists when the items are quite long.

c) He walked; into the room he had never been inside before.

d) Jim had made a huge pile he owned; a large percentage of the Nile.

Apostrophes

Teachers love complaining that 'young people these days' don't know how to use apostrophes. Do this page and you'll be able to knock them sideways with your stunning apostrophe know-how.

Q1 Read the following sentences a)-g). Copy down the sentences where it's, its, there's and theirs are wrong and change them so they're right.

a) Our son might not be perfect, but their's is atrocious.

b) Theres a small cat which lives in our barn.

c) Its sunny outside — why stay indoors?

d) The driver wanted the car repaired because its' gearbox was making funny noises.

e) I really like the theatre; theirs a good one in my home town.

f) It's hardly surprising that no children like Blue Peter: all their parents do.

g) "Its a Wonderful Life" is a film with Jimmy Stewart. Its shown every Christmas.

Q2 Apostrophes are used to show that something belongs.
Copy out the sentences below, putting apostrophes in the right places.

e.g. Philippas cows were a bit special.
Philippa's cows were a bit special.

a) The ostriches beaks were all shiny.

b) My brother Alexs band are playing in the pub on Saturday.

c) She gave him her mums favourite handkerchief, realising too late that it was covered in snot.

d) The childrens section of the menu was uninspiring.

e) Elmer McCurdys body was used as a fairground attraction for seventy years before people realised it was human and gave him a proper burial.

f) Marcus piano was six feet tall; he couldn't reach the pedals.

Q3 In informal writing, it's usual to combine or shorten certain words as if you were speaking. Copy the sentences below, combining or shortening the highlighted words.

Apostrophes are used to show that letters are missing.

a) I do not want to trouble you, but your Alsatian is in my garage.

b) The boxer will not fight without his lucky rabbit's foot.

c) Do you not think it's strange how television stars get thinner every year?

d) It is the best piece of music I have ever heard.

e) It is not that unusual for people to have two part-time jobs.

f) I cannot go to the gym. I will not go to the gym.
I do not want to go to the gym.

Honestly, she's just shy because you're here.

FYI — Philippa's cows could dance like Fred Astaire...

It was like a really bad cheese advert — they looked all knock-kneed and cow-like but then suddenly they were off, foxtrotting across the field. [Well, you think of summat interesting to say about apostrophes.]

Speech, Question and Exclamation Marks

"A page on speech and question marks?" I said. "Oh, and exclamation marks. No problem!"

Q1 Decide whether each of the following sentences needs to include speech marks. Copy out the ones which do, adding speech marks in the right places.

a) When asked if he was a communist, Ring Lardner Jr. replied I could tell you but I would hate myself in the morning.

b) Mae West used to quip that when she was good she was very good but when she was bad she was better.

Remember to add the right punctuation and capital letters to the sentences too.

c) Bette Davis said the famous line fasten your seat belts, it's going to be a bumpy night in the film 'All About Eve'.

d) When Tony Blair got into power, he kept saying education, education, education.

e) Frantz Fanon said that the revolutionaries wanted Algeria to be a place open to all, where any kind of genius could grow.

Q2 Read the following passage. Copy it out, putting in two question marks and three exclamation marks in appropriate places. You may need to make the odd letter capital too.

> **Jake burst through the door of the garage shop.**
> **"Freeze" he shouted. He was scared; he could feel the sweat rolling down his forehead and flooding his eyes. He moved towards the cashier, holding the bag out in one hand, grasping his fake gun in the other.**
> **"Oh my life" said the cashier, "Jake Smithson, what are you doing"**
> **Jake stopped in his tracks. He had been told that a pair of tights over the head would render any human being unrecognisable. Maybe 15 denier wasn't enough.**
> **"I'm not Jake Smithson," he said, backing away.**
> **"Yes you are, I used to serve you lunch at St Hilda's Primary School. Fancy that what are you getting up to these days" she said. Quietly, she pressed the police alarm under the counter.**

Q3 Copy out the following sentences, adding correct punctuation (including speech marks).

a) I'm hard to get said Slim all you have to do is ask.

b) My name is Maximus Decimus Meridus said the stranger and I will have my vengeance in this life or the next.

c) I think I'm falling in love with her said Fritz. Oh, I am sorry said Brian. So am I said Fritz.

d) She was awfully decent about that cheese said Caldicott. But I see she didn't leave much of the pickles said Charters.

e) I demand that you pay me one million dollars said Dr. Evil.

f) You say you're alone but your table's set for four said the policeman. That's nothing the man replied my alarm clock's set for eight.

Optional question: match the quotes with the films —
i) Cabaret
ii) To Have and Have Not
iii) A Night at the Opera
iv) Austin Powers
v) The Lady Vanishes
vi) Gladiator

Writing Interesting Sentences

Always vary the types of sentences you use, to keep the reader interested. That means making some sentences short and some long, and using tricks like rhetorical questions. Geddit?

Q1 Write these sentences out with a connecting word that joins together the two clauses.

a) Jim ran to the station .... he needed to catch the last train.

b) I am prepared to wait .... the governor decides what will happen.

c) Sergei Bubka thinks he is the best pole-vaulter in the world .... I am better.

d) I was about to go shopping .... the letter landed on the mat.

e) My ceramic frog collection is terrific .... it's worth a lot of money too.

Q2 Copy out each of these sentences, splitting each one into two shorter sentences. You may need to remove a few words from some for the new sentence to make sense.

a) Isabel had only got one ticket and she didn't want to give it away.

b) Pancakes with sugar and lemon are good but jam filling is also nice.

c) Daria flew over the wall and landed in a heap at the bottom of the ditch.

d) St Malo is really hot in the summer so you can go swimming in the sea.

e) Una was going to miss the plane unless she could grab a lift on the boy's skateboard.

Q3 Rewrite these sentences as rhetorical questions.

e.g. Christopher panicked; it was possible the vile mice had eaten the food.
Christopher panicked; surely the vile mice hadn't eaten the food?

a) We all know that paint dries very slowly.

b) We don't need to ask whether the governor will be back next year.

c) You seem to be saying that Muriel is lying, but that's ridiculous.

d) Cybil didn't know where to look; she thought that man had left five days ago.

Q4 The following paragraph is badly written. Make it sound better by making some sentences shorter and others longer — do it by splitting or combining sentences.

Rita Hayworth was born in 1918. She was born in America. Her original name was Margarita Cansino. Her family were Spanish. From the age of 13 she danced in a stage act with her father. She spent a lot of time practising her dancing. This meant she missed out on most of her education. In the late 1930s, she started to get small roles in films, but the American film industry was xenophobic and therefore didn't like the fact that she looked Spanish so her appearance was changed in the following ways: her black hair was dyed red and her hairline was made higher by electrolysis; in addition to this her Spanish-sounding name was changed to Rita Hayworth.

Writing Interesting Sentences

Easy tricks to make your writing more readable are: 1) vary how you start sentences, 2) vary the verbs you use, and 3) use pronouns when you can.

If you're not sure about verbs and pronouns, take a look at the CGP 'Essential Terms' book.

Q1 Swap the phrases and clauses of the following sentences around, so that they don't start with 'I'.

a) I dashed to the supermarket, even though it was raining.

b) I had to stop running; it didn't matter if the police caught me any more.

c) I will go on a fantastic holiday to Iceland, in the autumn.

d) I said, "Please go away."

e) I opened the satchel, suddenly worried.

Q2 Write down a more interesting verb which you could use instead of 'went' in each sentence.

a) Hayley went to the museum in her new car.

b) Mahmoud went to the box office, hoping he'd be in time to get a ticket.

c) Despite all the fuss she had made, Janice went in the aeroplane in the end.

d) Becky went around the shops after her gran, wishing she wasn't there.

e) The lamb went along the grass, looking very cute.

Q3 Write down a pronoun which could be used instead of the highlighted words in the following sentences.

Pronouns are words which stand in for a noun. They include: I, you, he, she, it, we, they, mine, yours, us, them.

e.g. Barnaby loved the smell of nachos. Barnaby also loved cricket.
Barnaby loved the smell of nachos. He also loved cricket.

a) I had hated Steve ever since Steve fouled me in football by dragging his studs down my leg.

b) The Five Nations tournament is on next week. I always watch the Five Nations on TV.

c) This is the biggest My Little Pony collection in the world. The My Little Ponies are all mine.

d) Sonia waited for Ahmed to finish work, then Sonia walked with Ahmed to the park.

e) Pete Postlethwaite is my sister's favourite actor. My sister really likes Pete Postlethwaite.

Q4 Rewrite these paragraphs. Replace some of the repeated nouns with pronouns to make it sound *slick*.

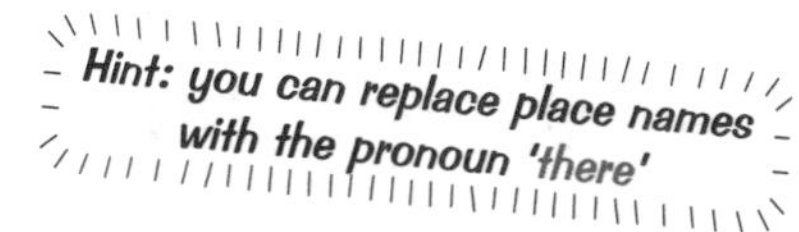

Hint: you can replace place names
with the pronoun 'there'

Frantz Fanon was born in the French colony of Martinique. Frantz Fanon trained as a psychologist in France. Frantz Fanon encountered racism in France. Frantz Fanon then decided to move to Algeria, which was a French colony. During his time in Algeria, Frantz Fanon worked at a hospital.

Frantz Fanon supported the Algerian revolution against French colonial rule which started in 1954. The Algerian revolution was very bitter and violent. In his role as a psychologist, Frantz Fanon treated both French soldiers who had tortured Algerian revolutionaries, and the victims of torture. Frantz Fanon wrote a book about the revolution, called 'A Dying Colonialism'. The book is very good.

Writing Interesting Sentences

Variety is the key to writing interesting sentences. Variety is the key to writing interesting sentences. Variety is the key to writing interesting sentences. Variety is the key to writing interesting sentences.

Q1 Active sentences make writing more interesting and engaging.
For each pair of sentences below, write down which is passive and which is active.

a) The hamster ate a large plate of fish and chips.
i) A large plate of fish and chips was eaten by the hamster.

b) Smoking is not allowed in the igloos.
ii) You shouldn't smoke in the igloos.

c) Reginald visited Buckingham Palace.
iii) Buckingham Palace was visited by Reginald.

d) A plate of spaghetti was thrown over the dog by Lisa.
iv) Lisa threw a plate of spaghetti over the dog.

Q2 Direct commands tell the reader exactly what to do.
Rewrite the following sentences, making them into direct commands.

Example: You should be wary of the ferocious chipmunks of Honolulu.
Beware the ferocious chipmunks of Honolulu.

a) I think you should keep quiet in the museum.

b) Maybe you shouldn't smoke in the flammable wigwam.

c) Why not try eating the frosted peas?

d) Why don't you go down to the dock of the bay?

Q3 You need to make sure that you write exactly what you mean. Copy out this table and fill in the blanks with phrases from the box below.

Don't spend ages drawing the table — it doesn't have to be a work of art.

What Leo said to John in the pub last night	How likely is it that Leo will buy the beer?
"I should buy some of your homemade beer."	
"I might buy some of your homemade beer."	
"If I was richer, I would buy your homemade beer."	
"I will buy some of your homemade beer."	
"I can buy your homemade beer."	

he'll definitely buy the beer
he won't buy the beer
he feels he ought to buy it, but it isn't definite that he will
he is able to buy it, but it isn't definite that he will
it's possible he will buy the beer

Vocabulary

Make an effort to use nice vocabulary. Oops. Make an effort to use vampish, varied and vivacious vocabulary. It gets you marks. What more do you want from life? Well, apart from...

Nice car like a Z3
Direct a film by age of 20
World record for high wages
Retire young

Q1 Identify the nouns in the following sentences.
Then copy out the sentences, adding an adjective to all of the nouns.

e.g. The man was happy because he'd bought a painting.

The rich man was happy because he'd bought a beautiful painting.

A noun is a thing (e.g. a person, place or object).
An adjective is a word that describes a noun.

a) The boy was scared that the dog would attack him.
b) Swimming is exercise.
c) Orpheus knew that he shouldn't look, but the temptation to see his wife was too much.
d) A wave came towards the shore and drenched the sunbathers.
e) In the park near my house there is an oak tree.
f) I didn't know until that moment how I would cope in such a situation.
g) It was three days before they realised that the hamster had escaped.
h) "It is a fact that Robert Mitchum is an actor," said my mum.

a verb is a 'doing' or 'being' word

Q2 Write out the sentence below with each of the endings a)-e). Change the verb "said" to a more interesting verb each time. Choose from the verbs in the grey box below.

Maria turned to Emma and said,

a) "I think we should be quiet; no one else is talking in here."
b) "Get out of my sight, you ungrateful, horrible woman."
c) "The hills are alive with the sound of music."
d) "Not another gas bill."
e) "All the other waitresses get better tips than me."

whispered
bellowed
groaned
griped
warbled

Q3 Copy out these sentences, putting an adverb with each verb.

adverbs are words which describe a verb

e.g. The spy walked over to the desk.

The spy walked calmly over to the desk. OR Calmly, the spy walked over to the desk.

a) Jane welcomed the professor.
b) The captain shouted at his daughter.
c) I walked down to the riverbank.
d) The cat eyed the salmon.
e) "Surely not the Maltese Falcon?" said Sam.
f) The robber was caught in the street.
g) The mastermind paced up and down the dank room.

Nope, it's the Falcon's Malteser.

Vocabulary

Always think about who you're writing for. If you're writing an imaginative story it might be OK to use all sorts of wacky words — but if you're writing a formal letter, you can't.

Q1 Copy and complete the table. For each underlined word think of two more words which have a similar meaning — one formal, one informal.

	The girl was nice.	The play was interesting.	The results were bad.	She's good at the piano.	The sea captain was old.
informal word	*friendly*				
formal word	*pleasant*				

Q2 *Read this extract from a letter.*

The pigeons, which invaded the church steeple two months ago, are really annoying. For starters, they squawk all the time so you can't hear yourself think, let alone hear the First Soprano. Plus, we have to put up with bird poo in the choir stalls. It really is too much to bear.

a) Write down any words and phrases which would be too informal if you were writing to an MP.

b) Rewrite the letter, replacing the informal words and phrases with more formal ones.

Q3 Make a list of all the adjectives and adverbs in this story, then rewrite the extract with more exciting adjectives and adverbs. Use words from the box below to help you.

Paul walked slowly down to the dock. The blue boat was still there, docked at the end of the quiet jetty. He hoped very much that the man had gone. There was a storm gathering slowly overhead. He realised quickly that it had grown dark. He took off his shoes and climbed onto the deck. There was the old door, with the scorch marks from the fire still there. From beyond the door he heard a quiet voice:

"Come in my child. You are welcome here."

Paul was struck by an awful fear. He knew that voice.

These words are just suggestions. You don't have to use them all.

Adjectives: mysterious insidious eerie silent paralysing familiar gigantic perilous frightening deafening gloomy

Adverbs: timidly self-consciously rapidly feverishly suddenly distantly maddeningly passionately fearfully

I only know two words...

Hmm. After that joke I'm going to crawl into a small hole and not come out again for eight and a half months, even if someone says "please". Meanwhile, on p37, you've got some spelling practice.

Spelling

There are four marks for spelling on the Shakespeare writing question — that's a fifth of the total marks. Remember to check your spelling when you read through your work at the end.

Q1 There are some words which are easy to mix up when you're in a hurry. Copy out the sentences below, choosing the right words from the brackets.

a) After the film we went back to [they're / their / there] house for a meal.

b) I wanted to go to the arcade, but when we got [they're / their / there] it was closed.

c) Slowly, I realised that I had no idea [where / wear] I was.

d) Your point of view depends on [whether / weather] or not you live near the worksite.

e) I [brought / bought] some food at the supermarket, before going home.

f) The new show by Pat Gussel is [quite / quiet] entertaining.

g) If you want to win the championship, you will need more [practice / practise].

h) If the manager leaves, the [effect / affect] on the players will be catastrophic.

i) I thought the car had moved, but when I looked again it was [stationary / stationery].

j) Their daughter, [who's / whose] in Manchester, is working in a pub.

Q2 Some words and phrases are really useful for the writing question. Sketch out the table below, correcting the spelling of the words in the white boxes.

Useful Words and Phrases for the Writing Question		
Starting a formal letter:	**Ending a formal letter:**	**Beginning a speech:**
Deer Sir / Madame Deer Mrs Jones	Yours sincerly Yours faithfuly	Welcom Good evning
Persuasive phrases:	**Impersonal phrases**	**Phrases to link paragraphs**
We all now that What we shud do now Surly we could	It can be argeud Some poeple believe One point of viuw is	On the othre hand A second raison for this is Anuther importnt concern is

Q3 This paragraph's bursting with bad spelling. Make a list of the words spelt incorrectly, then rewrite the paragraph with correct spelling.

Check your new spellings afterwards with a dictionary. There are 22 mistakes.

Occassionally, I like to visit the centre of town. You can see all the goverment builings which are really big and impressif. There are lots of poeple in the streets, walking and luaghing. The atmospere's brilliant. My favourite place is definitly the cathdral witch is nine hondred years old. Inside the cathdrale it's very cold but the stayned glass windews are beuatiful. There's also a coffee shop their which sells delicous cakes. Seperate from the cathdral is a small chapel which is notorius for haveing nuns buryied inside the walls.

Writing for the Reader or Audience

In the exam you'll have to pretend you're writing for a particular reader or audience, e.g. people in school assembly, readers of the school magazine, a local businessman, a friend...

Q1 a) These pieces of writing have been written for different types of reader or audience. Match up each piece of writing (A-D) with its intended reader or audience (i-iv).

(A) Last week, a local schoolboy got more than he bargained for when he added his mother's rhubarb crumble to a tank of algae. The result of this bizarre experiment? A teacher described it in one word: "Mayhem." The boy, aged 13, cannot be named for legal reasons.

(B) Last week, I did a really interesting experiment in my school. I tried adding rhubarb crumble to a tank of algae. Do you know what algae is? It's a sort of moss that grows on the surface of ponds. After three days, I found that the algae was growing bigger and bigger.

(C) Did I tell you that I did an amazing experiment in school last week? We were adding different things to tanks of algae to see what would happen. I added my mum's rhubarb crumble. Blimey, that was a mistake! The algae grew absolutely enormous; it was bigger than Gavin's bike.

(D) My teacher suggested that I should describe my algae experiment to you, in the hope that you could shed some light on the results. The algae was from a local pond in Haverthwaite. About 50 cm^3 was used in a 5 litre tank of water. One standard portion of crumble was added.

(i) A friend

(ii) Readers of a local newspaper

(iii) An expert

(iv) Pupils of a local primary school

b) Write a sentence explaining why each of the texts suits the reader or audience you chose in a). Think about the words, tone and style used.

Q2 Rewrite this newspaper article as if you are telling the same information to a friend in a letter. Make sure you lay it out like a real letter, and start and sign off properly.

Hamster Eats Puma Alive

A local zoo was thrown into chaos yesterday, when a pet rodent entered the puma enclosure and attacked a male puma.

The hamster was brought to the zoo by her owner, 9-year-old Lizzie Thomas. The girl's parents were unaware that she was carrying the rodent in her coat pocket at 3 pm yesterday, when it escaped.

It ran into the enclosure and collected large quantities of the puma's fur in its pouches, before being pulled off by a keeper.

The puma survived, but suffered hair loss

Writing for the Reader or Audience

There'll be information in the writing question which tells you who the reader or audience is. Have a gander at the sample exam question below, then do the questions that follow it.

This is an extract from a school newsletter:

> **The Karl Smith Young Travel Writer Award**
>
> In memory of Karl Smith, the school's gardener from 1978 to 2003, the school is introducing an annual award for the best piece of travel writing by a pupil. This year's entries should include:
>
> - a description of a favourite holiday destination, in Britain or abroad,
> - details of the language, architecture/scenery, food and climate.
>
> Entries will be judged by the headteacher.
> The local Herald newspaper has agreed to print the winning entry.

Write an entry for the award. You should make your report believable, but your account can be imaginary or based on real experiences.

30 marks

Q1 Who is going to read your entry to the award? Choose from options i)-iv).

i) Karl Smith, the school gardener

ii) The headteacher and the English teachers

iii) The headteacher and possibly readers of the local paper

iv) Iain Duncan-Smith

NB: You don't have to answer the actual exam question.

Q2 Write down all the words from the box which you think describe the tone your entry should have. Write a sentence to explain each choice.

jokey	persuasive	sarcastic	angry	atmospheric
indignant	offensive	negative	fairly formal	evocative
bored	very informal	imaginative	peculiar	positive

Q3 Here's a paragraph from an entry to the "Karl Smith Travel Writer Award". Rewrite the paragraph. Make the tone match the words you chose in Q2.

Hint: start by chopping out bits that seem unsuitable

> The food in Brittany is just brilliant. I bet you don't believe me but I've never tasted anything better and neither has my mum. First off, you don't have to eat rubbish, clichéd French food like croissants and baguettes. Boring!!! There are markets which sell fresh fruit and honey pies; you can eat them for breakfast instead. Though actually my sister got ill on the third day and wasn't able to eat anything at all. Bernadette and Hervé, the French couple we stayed with, were dead nice and they went to the market every day. It was really sunny and you could just wander around buying food and getting a tan.

001110000101000 — writing for robots...

0100000101111010010101010000111BILLGATES0100000101001110100000001111011101010111010101001111 00100ATEMYMOTHERBOARD101001010100110001100110011010100100100110011001001010101111011010010011001 1

Different Types of Writing

Exam questions always ask you to do a particular type of writing, e.g. a story, letter, speech... You've got to know tricks for all the different types in order to sweep the examiners off their feet.

Q1 Copy out the table and use words and phrases from the box below to fill in the blanks.

Type of Writing	Typical format/structure	Typical style/tone
Formal letter		Fairly formal and impersonal Written to specific reader(s)
	Begins with a welcoming introduction, followed by paragraphs and conclusion.	Written as if speaking directly to audience
Article/report	Has a headline, sometimes written in columns	
Story	Standard format, in paragraphs, with a beginning, middle and end	
Leaflet		Informative or persuasive Usually fairly formal
	Begins with "Dear..." Ends with informal sign-off, e.g. "Best wishes"	Personal, informal Written to specific reader(s)

Begins with address, and "Dear"
Ends with "Yours sincerely" or "Yours faithfully"

Informal letter

Speech

Entertaining/imaginative

Headings breaking up text, pictures with captions

Informative and impersonal

Q2 *Read through this information, then answer the questions below.*

Mr Tim Hazelwood is a refuse collector. He has been on strike for six weeks for better pay. The binmen in Thorncastle earn £6 per hour, and want this increased to £8 an hour. They think that because it's unpleasant work with unsociable working hours they deserve more pay. The council say they only have a limited budget and many other groups of workers are equally deserving of a pay rise. Mr Tim Hazelwood marched through the centre of Thorncastle on Saturday, wearing only a dustbin, to get publicity for the binmen's cause. He was arrested for indecent exposure.

a) Use the information in the box to write a short article for the local newspaper about Tim. Write in paragraphs and include a headline, but don't bother setting it out in columns.

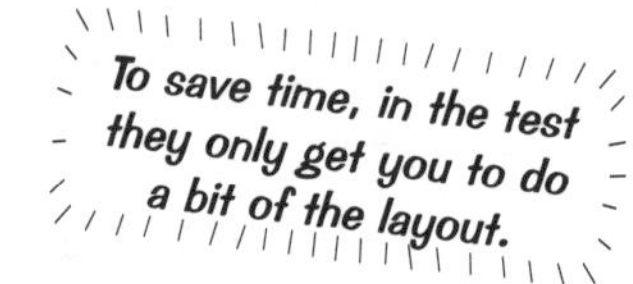

To save time, in the test they only get you to do a bit of the layout.

b) Write a formal letter from the Refuse Collector's Strike Association to Thorncastle's MP explaining why you want more pay. Start your letter "Dear Sandy Johns MP".

c) Write a short leaflet, to be sent out by the council, telling local residents about the strike. Explain that they'll have to take their own rubbish to the skip during the strike. Lay out your leaflet in paragraphs, and with headings, but don't do any illustrations.

Formal and Informal Writing

For any bit of writing in the SAT, work out whether the tone should be formal or informal, e.g. a tabloid article would be pretty slangy, whereas broadsheets are very formal.

Q1 Read the following sample exam question. Should the answer to the question be very formal, fairly formal or informal? Explain your answer.

> **New Science Block Brings Joy to School**
>
> Your local MP is visiting your school to open a new building. This is a memo from your headteacher:
>
> > We would like a select pupil to give a short speech at the opening of the new science block.
> > The speech should include:
> > - A welcome and thank you to the MP for attending the event
> > - A light-hearted description of the problems with the old science block
> > - A conclusion describing how happy the pupils are that there is now a new science block
>
> Write a speech to be given at the opening of the new building. *30 marks*

Q2 Rewrite the following paragraphs, making them sound more formal. Keep the same meanings.

a) Hi everyone, I'm here to tell you about all the stuff that's been happening during the last few weeks at the school. I'll then be showing you around, giving you a chance to chat to some of the kids and letting you have a few drinks and biscuits.

b) Switzerland is fantastic! There's so much you can do — snowboarding, skiing, walking and shopping. There's even bears you can feed in Basle, though it's pretty cruel that they're kept in captivity, when you think about it.

c) This paper can reveal exclusively that the main lottery draw has been fixed *three times* in the last year! Our suspicions were aroused when we discovered that supporters of the governing party had been winning significant sums on the lottery. We didn't want to believe it.

Q3 Rewrite the following letter, making it informal in format and tone.

> The Old Coach House
> Bowden
> RH3 7RL
>
> The Grange
> Oxton
> LH4 8PW
>
> Dear Josephine Baker,
>
> I am writing to ask your advice on a rather personal matter. Since I was young, I have enjoyed gymnastics, and had hoped to continue taking part in this sport for the rest of my life.
>
> Recently, however, I have started to suffer from rheumatism, which I believe is common among people of my advanced years.
>
> I have heard that, before you retired, you spent some years as a homeopathist. Do you have any recommendations for herbal remedies which might ease my pain, and enable me to backflip again? Any advice would be gratefully received.
>
> Yours sincerely,
> Bessie Smith

Does my bum look big in this?

Writing to Inform, Explain and Describe

The examiners split all the different styles of writing up into <u>four</u> "writing purposes". The first is to '<u>inform, explain or describe</u>' — basically, telling the reader some information.

Q1 Which of these types of writing are of the 'inform, explain, describe' type? Choose one or more from options i)-v) and explain your choices.

i) Instructions for a new pupil on what to do on their first day of school.

ii) A political leaflet telling people to vote Liberal Democrat.

iii) An account of what a place is like — its scenery, climate and architecture.

iv) A newspaper article commenting on the two sides of an argument between the council and a burger restaurant.

v) An article about a person you admire and the contribution they have made to your local area.

Q2 a) Below are three possible introductions to an 'inform, explain, describe' article (1-3). Match them up to the readers they have been written for (A-C).

1) Orson Welles was a really important director. He made a famous film, called 'Citizen Kane', a long time ago. It had a massive impact on how films were made, and how people told stories on film. This article is going to explain what was so special about 'Citizen Kane'.

2) Orson Welles is one of the most written about and controversial directors in film history. As you know, his most famous film 'Citizen Kane' (1941) has recently been the subject of criticism. In this article, I want to return the focus to what made 'Citizen Kane' a great film, and the many ways it changed the course of film history.

3) Orson Welles is one of the most exciting directors in film history. You have probably heard of his most famous film, 'Citizen Kane', made in 1941. What you might not realise is the huge impact it had on how films were made and how stories were told on film. That's what this article is all about.

A) Adult readers of the local paper who have probably heard of 'Citizen Kane'.

B) Younger pupils at your school who probably know nothing about 'Citizen Kane'.

C) The readers of a local film newsletter, who know quite a lot about 'Citizen Kane'.

b) For each introduction, explain how you can tell which audience it's written for.

Who's this? See p58.

Q3 Write two paragraphs about your favourite film. Describe the plot and explain why you think it's good. Pretend the reader hasn't heard of the film before.

My favourite film is Kodak...

Informing, explaining and describing are pretty similar. Informing is telling someone useful information, explaining is telling someone what information means and describing is telling someone all the details... you can often do all three at once.

Writing to Inform, Explain and Describe

Be clear when you're writing to 'inform, explain or describe'. Write about things in a logical order and explain tricky words. Use interesting vocab too — don't let it get dull...

Q1 Rewrite these paragraphs. For each one, put the sentences into a logical order.

a) It has an unusually hot climate. Past the olive groves, there is a river which is known locally as the 'Devil's River'. In Normandy, there is a very beautiful valley called the Gorge Rancré. The name originated in an ancient local myth that an animal had to be drowned in the river each year to keep the devil happy. This means that olive groves and vines can flourish there.

b) Anne was executed as a result. Therefore, charges of adultery were brought against Anne. This was important to Henry because he wanted a male heir to the throne. These charges were probably untrue, but it didn't matter because Henry was so powerful. Henry VIII decided he wanted to get rid of Anne Boleyn because she had failed to bear him a son.

Q2 Copy out these sentences taken from an 'inform, explain, describe' answer, changing the highlighted words to words from the cloud. Choose vocab that makes the sentences clearer.

a) The doctor will give you some stuff to do at home, so you can strengthen the muscle.
b) Do you like nice food? Then this is the article for you.
c) The new headmaster is very quiet and a bit scary. He knows too much about me.
d) Telescopes are great because they let you see things far away.

proper · facts · poverty · delicious
incredibly · nonsensical · poor quality
distant objects · exercises · sarcastic

Q3 The following sentences contain words which you might think are easy, but other people could find tricky. Rewrite each sentence, adding a short definition or explanation of the tricky word.

e.g. The ingredients for the recipe include fennel.
The ingredients for the recipe include fennel, which is a green, leafy vegetable.

a) The computer has a spell-checker.
b) My grandfather was an air-raid warden.
c) Liverpool is a multicultural city.
d) The striker was clearly offside.

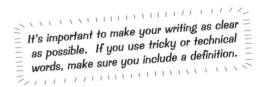

It's important to make your writing as clear as possible. If you use tricky or technical words, make sure you include a definition.

Q4 The following descriptive paragraph is really dull. Rewrite it making it more interesting, but keeping the same meaning. Try adding adjectives and adverbs and changing the verbs.

I went to the local funfair at the weekend. The rides were good. I went on the waltzer, but it made me feel ill. Then I went on the roller-coaster, and it was great. I liked going upside down, and seeing all the people on the ground. When I got off the roller-coaster I saw a friend from school but he went away before I could speak to him. Before I left I ate some candyfloss, which was really good.

Some of the really dull bits have been highlighted to get you started.

Writing to Persuade, Argue and Advise

The second type of writing exam question is 'persuade, argue and advise'. It's all about persuading someone to either agree with your point of view, or to take your advice on an issue.

Q1 Which of the following are tricks you can use to make your writing more persuasive? Choose one or more from options i)-v) and write them down.

i) Keep your writing polite. Don't intentionally offend people who disagree with your views.

ii) Use humour, contrast and repetition to put people off your main point.

iii) Use descriptive words to emphasise your points.

iv) Ally yourself with the reader by saying "us" and "we" and using rhetorical questions.

v) Back up your points with elephants.

Rhetorical questions are ones which don't expect an answer, e.g. "Surely we all know that Darwin was right?"

Q2 Rewrite the following sentences, changing the language to make them sound less vague and more convincing.

a) People should maybe think about the effect smoking could have on their health before they try cigarettes.

b) One question we might ask is, "If the government have evidence about why we should eat spinach, would they mind sharing it with us?"

c) If you don't want to go on the trip, it's probably best if you ask your mother to write a letter to the teacher explaining why.

Q3 Using adjectives makes your writing more persuasive, and adjectives work really well in groups of three. Copy down the sentences and fill in the blanks with adjectives.

***e.g.* We need to keep the local park; it is peaceful, beautiful and unique.**

a) I enjoy swimming because it is relaxing, fun and ....

b) It's important to read the newspapers because they are thought-provoking, ... and ....

c) We all know that homework is .... , ... and ....

There's more than one possible answer for each of these.

Q4 If you are writing to offer someone advice, you should suggest things — not insist on them. Change the following commands into suggestions.

e.g. You must do what the teacher says.

It would be a good idea to do what the teacher says.

a) You have to take part in the race.

b) Leave your job.

c) Come swimming at the leisure centre tomorrow.

d) Make your mind up.

I suggest that you leave the pool now.

Writing to Persuade, Argue and Advise

You can't ignore other people's points of view. To argue that your opinion is right, you need to say why other opinions are wrong. "You're wrong cos you smell of poo" doesn't cut the mustard.

Q1 Are the following paragraphs persuasive, or not? Explain each of your answers.

a) You should vote for Claire Harris if you want to see an improvement in employment and a clamping down on crime in the local area. These are areas in which she is very strong; her Young Offenders Scheme is ample evidence of this. On the other hand, you could vote for Edward Jones. He has agreed to increase spending on health and education, which are important issues for many people.

b) You should vote for Claire Harris because she is intelligent, honest and cares about the local area. Her scheme to help young offenders back into employment has been a major success and the envy of other constituencies. People backing Edward Jones forget the appalling crime and unemployment rates which this constituency suffered the last time he was in power.

Q2 Use the evidence from the boxes below to make two properly backed-up paragraphs, following on from the opening lines a) and b).

a) The death penalty should not be reintroduced in Britain.

b) The death penalty should be reintroduced in Britain.

Keeping people in prison costs the government money — for buildings, staff, food and healthcare. People who have committed horrific crimes and are sentenced to life imprisonment are wasting government resources.

There have been several recent cases in Britain where long-serving prisoners have been found innocent because of new evidence. If we had the death penalty in Britain these people would have been wrongly executed long ago.

Lord Justice Hodgeman has said on this issue, "Although I have great faith in the British legal system, we should not lie to ourselves that it is infallible."

Reintroducing the death penalty would also act as a deterrent to criminals. It would show them that the legal system in Britain is strong and won't let them get away lightly with their crimes.

Q3 Write a short article for your school newsletter arguing **either** that cars should be allowed in the school playground **or** that cars should be banned from the school playground. Mention all of the points from the table below in your article.

Why Cars Should be Allowed in the Playground	Why Cars Shouldn't be Allowed in the Playground
It is hard for teachers to find other parking nearby.	They increase the amount of noise outside school.
It is the safest place for teachers to leave their cars.	Children might be run over and injured or killed.
As long as people drive slowly, it should be safe.	It means there is less space for children to play and exercise.

Writing to Imagine, Explore and Entertain

This is the third type of writing question. Imaginative and entertaining writing means getting the reader involved in a text using pace, suspense, humour and interesting language. Writing to explore means thoughtful writing about your personal experiences and reactions to events, e.g. in a diary.

Q1 A good story follows a good structure. Put these parts of a story in the right order.

i) a satisfying ending, which resolves the crisis
ii) a crisis
iii) a gripping opening to the story
iv) development of the plot, characters and setting established in the opening

crisis = a period of trouble or danger

Q2 Comparisons make descriptions of characters and settings more interesting. Copy and complete the sentences below, adding a word to each to complete the comparison.

e.g. Paul was so scared that he wobbled like a ....
Paul was so scared that he wobbled like a jelly.

The posh word for this sort of comparison is 'simile'

a) Ilona turned to the headteacher furiously and screamed like a ....
b) As he crept over to the side of the ship, Bob's shoes squeaked like ....
c) The atmosphere in the dentist's waiting room was like a ....
d) The chips looked gorgeous. Henry was as hungry as a ....

There's more than one possible answer for each of these.

Q3 Write a description of each thing below, using alliteration to make it more effective.

e.g. snake → ***The snake slithered subtly across the sparkling sand.***

a) storm b) cat

i.e. start off a few words with the same letter

Q4 Write a list of onomatopoeic words that you could use to describe each thing.

e.g. piano music → ***crash, plink-plonk, trill, murmur...***

a) explosion b) Grand Prix start

onomatopoeia = words that sound like the noise they describe

Q5 Rewrite this paragraph, replacing the highlighted clichés with more interesting language.

Then, the icing on the cake — who should walk in but my old nemesis, Miss Rumple! That was a shock to the system. I had no room for manoeuvre; I had to take the bull by the horns. So I took the catapult from my pocket, saying to myself, "It's not over until the fat lady sings."

Q6 Match up each of the characters below to four words from the box that you might use to describe them.

If you don't know a word, look it up.

a) Henry, a shy boy who likes running.
b) Mrs Henderson, a bossy shop keeper.
c) Pau, a pop sensation from Catalonia.

authoritarian	athletic	intimidating	fashionable	famous	timid
glamorous	musical	ancient	introverted	garrulous	fit

Writing to Imagine, Explore and Entertain

Keep the tone and style the same all the way through a piece of imaginative writing. If you're writing from someone else's point of view, don't slip up and start writing as yourself.

Q1 Which of the following paragraphs has more suspense? Explain your answer.

i) There was a cat in the bag. Josephine didn't know what was in there and wanted to find out, so she put her hand in the bag. She screamed when she felt the cat's fur.

ii) Josephine approached the bag cautiously. She had to find out what was in there. As she reached in, her fingers felt something furry. She screamed. It was a cat!

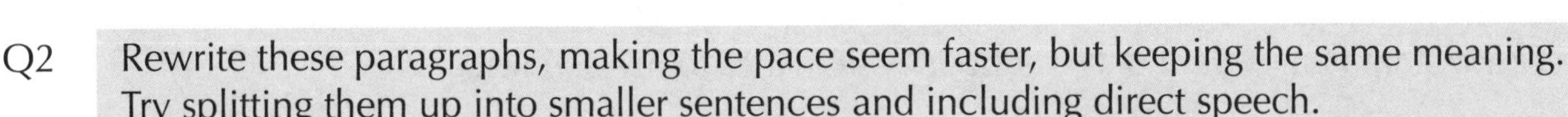

Q2 Rewrite these paragraphs, making the pace seem faster, but keeping the same meaning. Try splitting them up into smaller sentences and including direct speech.

a) She was sitting quietly on a bench in the park and didn't seem scared. I rushed up and told her that she should run away as fast as possible, but she didn't seem to understand.

b) The warrior Xenodwarf wielded his sword and told his enemy to prepare for death. To his surprise the enemy refused to surrender and did a nifty flying kick towards his right ear.

Q3 You can sometimes be asked to write from someone else's point of view — imagining that you are that person. The following paragraph has been written using third person narration. Rewrite it as if <u>you</u> are Sarah telling the story (from the point of view of 'I').

> **Sarah was led through the servants' quarters towards the big kitchens. She felt scared, and trembled visibly. The only time she had been to the manor before was to deliver a message for her sister who worked there as a lady's maid. Even then she had been frightened. There were stories about the manor; people in the village said there were so many corridors under the house it was like a maze. A boy had been lost down there, in a game of hide and seek. The rumour was that he was still alive.**

Q4 Read the newspaper article below, and write a letter by Sterling Hayden to his daughter describing the events.

> ### Sea Captain Reveals His Salsa Hell
>
> A lone yachtsman was unable to land on shore for three months, because of his newly-developed addiction to salsa dancing. Wizened former sea captain Sterling Hayden told this newspaper that he had first started dancing when he watched a salsa-based exercise video his daughter lent him to help him keep in shape.
>
> Says Sterling, "At first it was fun; I enjoyed tapping my toes. But soon I was in the throes of addiction. I couldn't steer or keep course because the urge to dance was so strong. After three months, I finally recovered after finding a Bach CD under a life jacket."

Q5 Imagine you have an older sister or brother who's recently got married. Write a short diary entry exploring your thoughts about the marriage. Use the points below to help you.

- What is your sibling's new husband/wife like? Do you get on with them?
- How did the news they were getting married make you feel? (e.g. jealous, excited)
- What was the ceremony like? Did you play any part in it? (e.g. bridesmaid)

Writing to Analyse, Review and Comment

The last type of writing you could get in the exam is 'analyse, review and comment'. This means discussing a subject without ranting about your opinions — you have to sound detached.

Q1 Make writing sound impersonal when you're writing an analysis. Rewrite these sentences, changing the language to be more detached and neutral.

e.g. I don't like the programmes on children's television; they're really patronising.

Some teenagers don't enjoy the programmes on children's television; they think that the programmes are patronising.

a) I think children over 14 should be allowed to go on holiday by themselves; I know that I enjoy very different holiday activities to my parents.

b) I think it's disgusting that confectionery and fast-food manufacturers can advertise on television, persuading children to eat food that is really unhealthy.

c) Surely everyone knows that the government is trying to introduce stealth taxes on mobile phones?

Q2 Sweeping statements make you sound biased. Rewrite these sentences to make them sound more cautious. Use words and phrases from the box to help you.

a) The greenhouse effect is having a terrible effect on the Earth's environment.

b) If the Green Party got into power, it would be great for Britain and great for the environment.

c) Dogs make very good pets because they force people to go for walks and get some fresh air.

d) Trains are never on time.

Don't use any of the phrases more than once.

It is possible that... Some people believe... might could perhaps One point of view is that... maybe often sometimes can

Q3 Use the following plan to write a short newspaper article commenting on the building of a new football stadium in the centre of town.

Should there be a new football stadium in the centre of Sudley?	
Group of people:	**Their opinions about the new stadium:**
Managers of the football club	It will be bigger than the old one, so more fans can watch the match. More profit can be made.
Some local residents	Worries about the noise, traffic congestion and football hooligans in the centre of town.
Local shopkeepers and businesses	Might bring more people into the town centre. Pubs and food outlets might profit.

Writing to Analyse, Review and Comment

Analytical writing is very different to persuasive writing. Your aim here is to show the examiner you've considered different opinions and evidence as objectively as possible.

Q1 You need to look at both sides of the argument when you're writing to 'analyse, comment and review'. Copy the table below. Write in three reasons to support each opinion.

Should the Royal Family have their privileged position taken away and become a normal family?	
Opinion: YES	**Opinion: NO**
Reason 1:	**Reason 1:**
Reason 2:	**Reason 2:**
Reason 3:	**Reason 3:**

Q2 Conclusions to essays can be tricky — you have to give your opinion, but still sound reasonable and objective. Explain why each of these conclusions is good or bad.

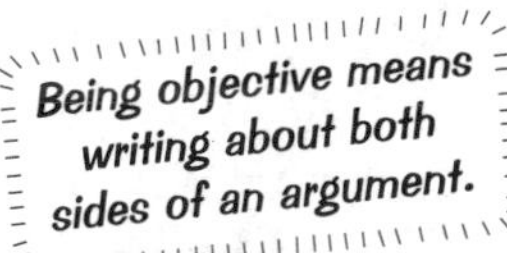

Being objective means writing about both sides of an argument.

a) In conclusion, some people are very worried by the rapid destruction of the rainforests. The rainforests are very hard to replace and wildlife are losing their habitats. On the other hand the people who live there need farmland to make a living. It's a really difficult issue and hard to reach a conclusion about.

b) As shown in the above essay, there are strong arguments on both sides. I personally believe that alternatives need to be found to the deforestation of the rainforests because of the long-term bad effects on the environment. People may gain farmland from clearing rainforests, but the land soon becomes infertile. Other solutions need to be found to create livelihoods for people in the region, so that the rainforests and environment can be protected.

I wholeheartedly agree.

c) I am going to conclude this essay with my personal opinion about the topic. I strongly believe that the rainforests shouldn't be cut down. Any other views are deeply misguided. It shows a real lack of intelligence that people could destroy something so precious. We should all campaign to stop the destruction of the rainforests.

Q3 Look back at the table you wrote for Q1. Write a conclusion for the essay.

Just write the conclusion, not the whole essay.

Don't believe a word Anna says — analyse...

It's a confusing world we're living in. By the end of this section you'll have it sussed. Well, you'll know the difference between persuading, analysing, imagining and informing anyway.

Paragraphs

Whatever kind of writing you're asked to do in the exam, you have to write in paragraphs. It gives your writing structure and gets you marks.

Q1 1-5 below are the reasons for starting a new paragraph. Match them with the paragraph changes in the bits of writing labelled a)-e).

(1) new point / topic (2) new person (3) different person speaks
(4) new time being described (5) new place being described

a The Red Scare of 1919 was a time of paranoia in America about left-wing radicals. The Sacco and Vanzetti trial is a famous example.
The McCarthy communist witchhunts were a similar phenomenon. Prominent figures, for example in the film industry, were accused of being communists.

b Algeria was colonised in 1830 and remained under French rule until the revolution of the 1950s. The revolution was very violent and lasted from 1954 to 1962.
Egypt was quite different. It was never fully colonised, but was under a British protectorate from 1881.

Trapped! Hope I can get out of here by Christmas...

c John walked over to the ostrich and raised his hat.
"How do you do sir?" he asked politely. However, the ostrich did not reply.

d Kirsty felt really angry about the play. She kicked the old lady sitting in front of her in frustration.
The old lady turned round and grinned a terrible grin. Slowly, she raised her stick.

e Ernest Hemingway used to live in Key West in Florida. His favourite bar there was called Sloppy Joe's.
If you go to Sloppy Joe's now it's in a different building and is just a tourist trap.

Q2 A good paragraph sticks to one topic. Work out which sentences in the following paragraph are rambling off the main topic. Then write out a corrected version.

> Pompeii was a small city of no great importance in the Roman world. Seneca does mention the town of Ostia in two of his letters. One of the few mentions Pompeii gets in ancient texts is in relation to a fight which broke out at the amphitheatre in which several people were killed. We can glean more information from the archaeological excavations at the site. From the size of the site it is estimated that it had about twenty thousand inhabitants. Pliny didn't live there, although he was killed by inhaling ash from the eruption. Evidence from the site includes: buildings, the contents of people's houses, wall paintings, graffiti and plaster casts of people who died in the eruption.

Q3 Copy out this bit from a short story, starting new paragraphs where needed.

> As Myrna sat down at the kitchen table she already felt full. So far she had eaten five blueberry tarts, ten Easter eggs, a rhubarb crumble and 76 fun-size chocolate bars. Ali ran into the room and saw the last piece of evidence, the double-cream layered pavlova still there on the kitchen table. "Come on, he's almost here!" he yelled. "I'm trying," groaned Myrna. Meanwhile, the dastardly Mr Smiker was walking slowly across the fields, his nose twitching in the breeze. The unmistakable scent of a missing double-cream layered pavlova filled his monstrous nostrils. He smiled a terrifying smile. Even his teeth were evil.

Paragraphs

Look — more paragraph questions. Fun, fun, fun.

Q1 Here's a paragraph from a persuasive essay. Rearrange the sentences into the following order: 1) main point, 2) development of main point, 3) evidence (quotes and statistics).

Seventy-five students make use of the bus service; that's a lot of extra cars. If our school bus was discontinued each child would have to travel to school individually. As the headteacher has said, "The pollution caused by the extra cars travelling to the school would have a bad effect on the environment." We all know that school buses are environmentally friendly.

Q2 Read the following paragraphs. Write a first sentence for each paragraph which introduces the main point it is making.

a) From this point of view, a foetus is a human being with the same value as a baby which has already been born. Julia Donovan of the Pro-Life League says that "People have to put aside their concerns for the mother and think about the child; abortion is effectively murdering a baby." Midwife Deborah Ash agrees, claiming that people who support abortion have not considered the realities of the operation.

b) From this point of view the rights of the mother are more important than those of the foetus. For example, Bethany Maine of the Women's Rights Association argues that "People who argue against abortion often have no understanding of the difficult situations some women face. Women must have control of their own bodies and be able to choose whether or not to bring a baby into the world."

Q3 If you're describing an event you should write things down in the order they happened. Put these sentences in order and write them out as a paragraph.

- Hillary had been annoyed; she'd wanted to have an adventure, not to go home.
- Once, when Hillary was at primary school, she'd climbed over the playing field fence.
- Hillary had refused to be scared and had started walking as far from school as possible.
- After about two hours she had reached her own house.
- All her friends had run away because they were scared.

Q4 You can compare and contrast two things within a paragraph. Which of the following paragraphs does this well, and which does it badly? Explain your answer.

a Winter is brilliant. If you're lucky it snows and you can go sledging and have snowball fights. The only real problem is that people have more colds and the days are shorter. In summer the weather's hot and you get sunburn, although the days are longer.

b Winter is brilliant. If you're lucky it snows and you can go sledging and have snowball fights. I like skidding around on the ice too. The build-up to Christmas is great, and it gets dark early, which is fun and spooky. I don't like summer though.

Q5 Write a paragraph comparing cities and the countryside.

Linking Paragraphs

OK, so now your paragraph writing is so polished, you could eat your dinner off it. You've still got to make sure your paragraphs flow — i.e. follow on nicely from each other.

Q1 Write out the words or phrases below (i-xii) that are useful for linking paragraphs together.

i) furthermore
ii) another point of view is
iii) with hindsight
iv) gregarious types
v) too right
vi) a contrasting view is
vii) milking it
viii) however
ix) another example of
x) in addition to this
xi) beyond comprehension
xii) on the other hand

Q2 A new paragraph should use a linking word or phrase to join it to the paragraph before. Read these paragraphs and write an opening sentence for the paragraph that follows.

e.g. **Cary Grant was a suave actor, at his peak in the 1940s and 1950s. Originally he was from Bristol, and his real name was Archibald Leach.**

[The next paragraph is going to be about Ingrid Bergman, a movie star in the 1940s and 1950s.]

Another popular movie star from the 1940s and 1950s was the actress Ingrid Bergman.

a) **Many years ago white lead was used in face powder. This resulted in women suffering from lead poisoning, although they didn't know what the cause of the illness was.**

[The next paragraph is going to be about how nowadays people know white lead is dangerous and don't use it for make-up.]

b) **The opinion of the school's board of governors about truancy is fairly harsh. They suggest that pupils should be punished with detentions, and that the parents of repeat offenders should be sent warning letters and fines.**

[The next paragraph is about the opinion of the Parent's Association, which is less harsh.]

c) **Many young children enjoy cartoons. They are bright and appealing to look at and feature easily recognisable characters. A lot of imagination and humour is put into popular cartoons, and this attracts children's interest.**

[The next paragraph is going to be about how many parents disapprove of cartoons because they think they are mindless drivel.]

Q3 Write two paragraphs. In the first one describe the village, town or city where you lived when you were ten. In the second paragraph describe the primary school you went to there. Link the two paragraphs together smoothly.

Q4 Write two paragraphs: the first describing your views about fashion, the second describing your parents' views about fashion. Link the two paragraphs together smoothly.

Writing Good Introductions

The introduction is the first thing the examiner will read. So make sure it's a good 'un.

Q1 Pretend you are writing a speech to give to the Parent-Teacher Association of your school. Which of the following words and phrases, i)-x), would be good to use in your introduction?

i) Good morrow fair gentlemen
ii) Good evening
iii) Okey-dokey
iv) We are here tonight to discuss
v) We are here tonight to rant about
vi) In my introduction to this essay
vii) Hi, it's darn good you could all come tonight
viii) Welcome
ix) In conclusion
x) The key issue I am going to discuss is

Q2 In a persuasive essay you need to make sure your argument is clear in the introduction. Which of these introductions does this better? Explain why.

Remember — persuasive essays are very different from analysing essays.

i) The issue of security is important in modern schools. Tragedies have taken place when violent outsiders have been able to walk unchallenged into school grounds. If security isn't improved in all schools, we have to ask ourselves: how long will it be before another tragedy happens?

ii) The issue of security is important in modern schools. A lot of schools have increased security since a series of violent incidents over the last few years. Some people think this is the right course of action to protect children. Others believe it creates an unhealthy atmosphere of fear and paranoia.

Q3 Below is part of an essay plan. It's for an essay analysing the effect of advertising on children's television. Use the plan to write a full introduction to the essay.

Good points
1. money from advertising helps to fund non-BBC programming, including good children's programmes.
2. adverts are often entertaining, with imagination and humour that children enjoy.

Bad points
1. advertising persuades children to buy sweets and junk food which is unhealthy for them.
2. advertising encourages children to want expensive toys, which their parents might not be able to afford.

Language to use: remember to be impersonal/objective/cautious when analysing

Q4 The notepad below shows an author's notes for the introduction of an imaginative story, called 'Dancing Bob'. Use the information on the notepad to write an introduction to the story.

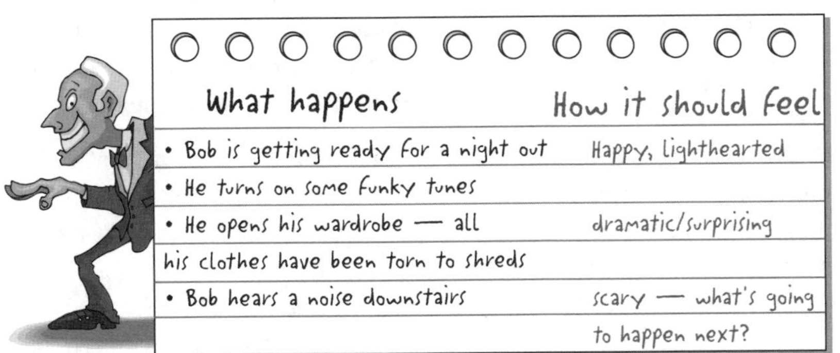

What happens
How it should feel
• Bob is getting ready for a night out
Happy, lighthearted
• He turns on some funky tunes
• He opens his wardrobe — all his clothes have been torn to shreds
dramatic/surprising
• Bob hears a noise downstairs
scary — what's going to happen next?

Don't write more than six sentences for your introduction.

Structuring the Middle Bit

The basic structure for all your writing should be: introduction, middle paragraphs and conclusion. To really impress the examiner you'll need to structure your middle paragraphs too.

Q1 The boxes i)-vi) below summarise the types of paragraphs in a typical persuasive essay. Put i)-vi) into a logical order and write them out.

i) Give a reason to support your argument. Back it up with evidence.

ii) Conclusion — bring together main points why your argument's right.

iii) Give a reason why people might not agree with your argument. Give evidence of why they are wrong.

iv) Give a second reason why people might not agree with your argument. Give evidence of why they are wrong.

v) Introduction — outline your main argument.

vi) Give a second reason to support your argument. Back it up with evidence.

Q2 These plans are for an essay analysing whether it's good to live in the countryside. One of them's not as well structured as the others. Decide which it is and say why.

i)
Introduction
Advantages
1. wildlife, great scenery
2. fresh air
3. good outdoor activities
4. less noise pollution
Disadvantages
1. public transport feeble
2. less access to good libraries/museums/cultural events than in a town
3. fewer jobs available
Conclusion

ii)
Introduction
Advantage 1 the countryside is a great place to live because of the wildlife, scenery and fresh air.
Advantage 2 There are some really interesting jobs e.g. in conservation.
Advantage 3 There are lots of brilliant outdoor activities, e.g. canoeing and rock climbing.
Conclusion

iii)
Introduction
1. adv: good outdoor activities
disadv: fewer cultural activities, e.g. theatres
2. adv: fresh air and less noise pollution
disadv: less public transport; often have to rely on car
3. adv: wildlife and scenery
disadv: fewer jobs than in towns
Conclusion

Q3 Write down the correct chronological order for these paragraphs.

chronological — in the order of when things happened

i) We now know that the body Schliemann found in Grave Circle A is unlikely to be that of Agamemnon. The graves date from c.1500 BC, while the Trojan War probably happened in 1200-1100 BC.

ii) The ruined cities of Tiryns, Mycenae and Pylos in Greece date from as far back as 1500 BC. They are mentioned in Homer's epic poems 'The Iliad' and 'The Odyssey'. For example, the character Agamemnon in 'The Iliad' is called the ruler of Mycenae.

iii) The ruins of Mycenae were excavated by the German archaeologist Heinrich Schliemann in the nineteenth century. He was a romantic man. When he found a golden death mask in Grave Circle A at Mycenae, he claimed that he had "seen the face of Agamemnon".

iv) Further excavations are still happening at Mycenae. Archaeologists want to find out more about ancient Mycenean religions; evidence so far includes frescoes, shrines and statues of goddesses. How much more can they find in the ruins of this great city?

Structuring the Middle Bit

The exam questions give you lots of hints you can use to structure your essay — and for the long writing question you get a planning grid so you can do a good, structured plan.

Q1 *Read the following short writing question and then do parts a) and b).*

> **Last Night Out Before Revision**
>
> Your school is organising a meal out for Year 9 pupils before revision begins for the SATs.
>
> For the attention of Year 9 pupils:
> The school has decided to pay for a free meal out on the eve of the revision period.
> The headteacher urges pupils to remember that:
> • the SATs will be over soon
> • all their hard work will be rewarded with good grades
> • pupils who don't work hard will regret it later
>
> Write a speech that the headteacher will give at the meal. *20 marks including 4 marks for spelling*

a) Write down three key topics you would need to cover in your answer to the question.

b) Write down your three key topics on a piece of paper as headings.
Then write down two points you could make under each heading.

Q2 *Read the following long writing question and accompanying planning page.*

> **Kill Your Speed**
>
> This is an extract from a newspaper article:
>
> > Speed limits must be reduced in urban areas. The current risk to lives from traffic is too great. If a driver runs over a pedestrian when he is doing 20 mph, there is a one in five chance he will kill them. This is already a high risk — so why are city speed limits usually as high as 30 mph? Being in a hurry is no excuse. Neither are the improvements in traffic control and pedestrian crossings.
>
> Write a letter to the newspaper in reply, arguing either for or against a reduction in city speed limits.
>
> *30 marks*

Use this page to plan your work.

arguments supporting your point of view	opinions which disagree with your point of view

a) Copy the planning page out onto an A4 sheet. Fill in two points under each of the main headings using information and ideas mentioned in the question itself.

b) Write down two more points, of your own, under each of the main headings.

c) Number the points you have under each heading in order of importance. Cross out any which seem unimportant.

By the end of c) you'll have a good essay plan — just the kind of thing you'll want in the exam.

Middle bit — Keeps your nose away from your feet...

Always put the most important points first — that way you'll have time to explain them properly and if you end up leaving anything out, it'll be the minor points. Helpful advice continues overleaf...

Pointing Out the Structure for the Reader

Structuring your essay is worth marks — so make sure your sleepy examiner realises what you're doing. Big signposts going "Hey buster, my conclusion's over here," ought to do the trick.

Q1 Which of the following introductions (i-iii) signpost clearly what the structure of the leaflet is going to be? Explain how.

i) Schools can help the environment; a few simple things can make a big difference. We all know that recycling is important, but so are many other issues, for example educating children about the environment. This leaflet is all about how you can make your school environmentally friendly.

ii) Schools can help the environment; a few simple things can make a big difference. This leaflet provides information about easy steps schools can take. Three main areas are covered: recycling and reusing materials, school bus services and educating pupils about the environment.

iii) Schools can help the environment, for example by recycling and reusing materials in class. This is very easy to do — try turning a painting over and doing another on the back. Simple! This leaflet will give you loads of other hints for making your school a greener place.

Q2 Signposting the structure of an essay is good, because it lets the reader know what to expect. Write out the phrases and sentences below that would be useful for this.

i) The main argument in favour of this will be dealt with first.
ii) The second half of this essay will discuss the disadvantages...
iii) Without a doubt, nothing can be done about this situation.
iv) There are three main issues at stake here; they will be discussed in turn.
v) The first half of this essay will discuss the advantages...
vi) The second reason for supporting this point of view...
vii) Finally, this essay will consider the impact on...
viii) This is a controversial topic.

Learn and use the good phrases — they'll really impress the examiners.

Q3 Below is part of an analytical essay discussing the advantages and disadvantages of building a new sports hall. Copy out the paragraphs, inserting phrases like those you chose in Q2 to signpost the structure of the essay.

The new sports hall is a major facility that the school currently lacks. At the moment children have to travel to the local leisure centre to do P.E. and this is a waste of valuable lesson time.

Exercise is a really important part of education. It helps make people healthy and happy. It would be good if the school could offer a wider range of sporting activities and a new sports hall would enable this.

The proposed site for the new sports hall is far from ideal. The plan is to build it on the site of the old and beautiful school garden. Many people disagree with this strongly.

This is the only place, other than the playground, where children can sit and relax at breaktimes. The importance of a peaceful place in a busy school cannot be dismissed lightly.

Writing Good Conclusions

Phew... on to the conclusion already. The conclusion is the last paragraph of your essay. It should bring everything together and tie it up nicely — in a triple reef knot perhaps.

Q1 Is the following statement true or false? Explain your answer.

"The conclusion is a good place to bring in new information. There is no need to be consistent with what has gone before in the essay — capturing the reader's interest is key."

Q2 Which three of the following things (i-viii) should you include in a conclusion?

i) a final statement about the topic
ii) a small Mercedes to bribe the examiner
iii) a summary of the main points in your essay
iv) all the points in your essay explained in detail
v) an introduction to a new topic
vi) a rant about what you think
vii) yesterday's mashed potatoes
viii) your own view on the topic

Q3 The main points made in a persuasive essay are shown by the bullet points below. Write a conclusion for the essay based on these bullet points.

Should testing on animals be allowed?

Main points made in essay:

- *I believe that any unnecessary testing on animals should be banned.*
- *Testing on animals is very cruel. Research shows that animals feel pain just like humans.*
- *Animals are often bred purely to be tested on. They are not given the chance to experience any freedom in their life at all.*
- *Make-up is still sometimes tested on animals, which seems unnecessary as this could be tested on humans instead.*
- *Some people argue that testing on animals is necessary in order to develop new medicines to cure diseases that cause many people to suffer. However, I believe that testing on animals should be kept to a minimum to stop animals suffering.*

Q4 An imaginative story needs a logical, satisfactory ending. Here's a summary of the middle section of the story 'Dancing Bob' (see page 53). Write an ending paragraph for the story.

What happens next

- There is a fire safety axe behind the door. Bob smashes the glass and takes the axe.
- He ventures downstairs — his dog is lying dead at the bottom of the stairs. Bob puts down the axe and howls with grief. Only his daughter Velma could have done this.
- Through the door Velma emerges. She laughs at Bob, and says "You always were a sap, forget about the dog, I want your money. Where's the safe?"
- Bob thinks quickly. "Velma" he says, "You're my only daughter, you can have all the money you want. It's in the cellar..."

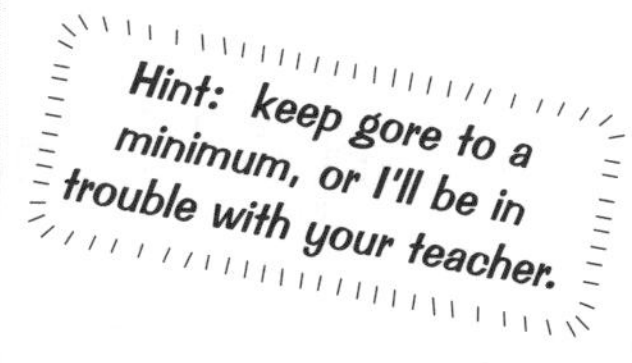

Hint: keep gore to a minimum, or I'll be in trouble with your teacher.

The end of the essay is nigh...

Don't go thinking "and they all lived happily ever after..." is going to do it, coz that won't even bring a twitch of a smile to those stoney-faced examiners. Write a conclusion and write it good.

The Long Writing Question

The long writing question is worth 30 marks. You need to think carefully about what you're going to write — and remember all the things you've practised in this section. Here's an example of a long writing question. The next three pages lead you through how to answer it well.

Should pupils do homework?

This is an extract from the 'Learning in Britain' website, written by teacher Edna Monich:

> We need to open up a discussion about how much homework pupils are given. Some of my Year 9 students have up to two hours of homework each evening. This makes them feel stressed and tired, and stops them from taking part in extracurricular activities. Homework may allow children to practise skills and learn information, but that is no excuse to give them excessive amounts of work.

Write an article for your school magazine about homework. Argue either that homework is useful, or that pupils should be given less homework.

30 marks

Q1 a) Who is your article supposed to be aimed at? Choose from options i)-iv).

i) teachers in the North West

ii) a mixture of teachers, pupils and parents

iii) the readers of the 'Learning in Britain' website

iv) Edna Monich

b) Write down the part of the question which lets you know who will read your article.

Q2 a) Write out the words below which you think describe the tone appropriate for the article.

friendly informal angry happy-go-lucky humorous formal polite offensive sarcastic

b) Explain why you picked those words.

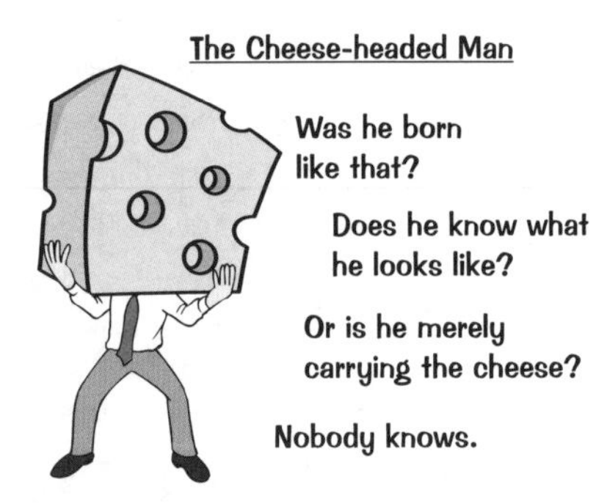

The Cheese-headed Man
Was he born like that?
Does he know what he looks like?
Or is he merely carrying the cheese?
Nobody knows.

Q3 a) What is the purpose of the article? Choose from options i)-iv).

i) to inform, explain or describe
ii) to persuade, argue or advise
iii) to imagine, explore or entertain
iv) to analyse, review or comment

b) Write a sentence explaining what this purpose means in your own words.

The Long Writing Question

There's a planning page on the exam paper to help you plan your answer to the long writing question. You're given 15 minutes to plan your answer. The planning page below goes with the SAT question on page 58. Copy it out onto a piece of A4 paper and then answer the questions below.

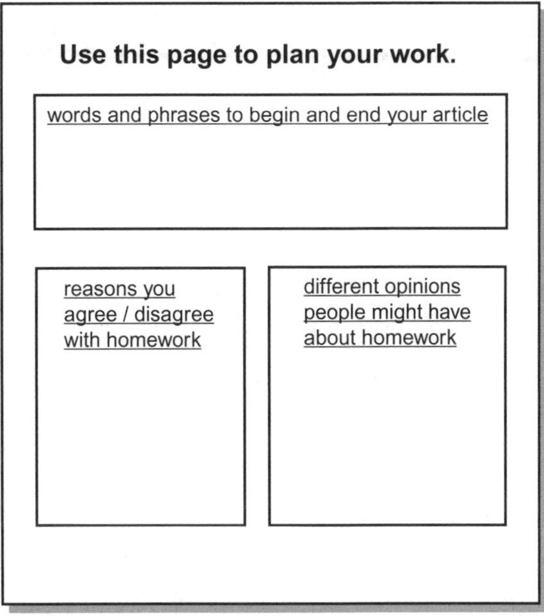

Q1 a) Which of the following sets of words and phrases do you think would be most appropriate to begin your article? Choose one set or words and phrases from options i)-iv).

i) good evening / I welcome you on behalf of my school / today I would like to talk about

ii) homework is an important issue / I believe that / should pupils be given less homework?

iii) hiya / people who don't agree are idiots / my mum says this as well

iv) would like to describe / the aim of this article is to give an informative account

b) Give a reason for your choice, and explain why each of the other options is wrong.

Q2 Fill in the box labelled "words and phrases to begin and end your article" on your planning page.

Q3 *Decide whether you are going to argue that you agree or disagree with homework.*

a) Read the question again and find two points in the question which support your view. Write them into the box on the planning page labelled "reasons you agree / disagree with homework."

b) Think of two more reasons why your opinion is right, and write them into the same box.

Q4 a) Read the question again, and find two points in the question which disagree with your opinion. Write them into the box labelled "different opinions people might have about homework."

b) Think of two more reasons why other people might not agree with your opinion and write them into the same box.

The Long Writing Question

It's not over yet. More questions about that homework question planning page coming right up...

Q1 a) Read through your planning page. Cross out any points which seem unimportant.

b) Number the points you've got in each box in order of how important / good they are. The best point in each box should be number 1.

c) Link together any points which seem similar or related — draw a line between them.

Q2 i) - iii) are all ways you could structure your article but only two of them are good ways. Decide which one would be a bad idea and explain why it's not as good as the others.

i) The reasons why you think your opinion is right go in the first half of the article. In the second half of the article you discuss different points of view people could have and why you think they're wrong.

ii) Each paragraph of your article compares a point for and a point against homework. You argue that the points which agree with your opinion are better.

iii) Each paragraph of your article gives a reason why your point of view is right and backs it up with examples and evidence. This means you don't have to discuss other points of view.

Q3 Is the following statement true or false? Explain your answer.

"It's OK to change your argument halfway through a piece of persuasive writing. Just make sure your conclusion matches the introduction and the examiner won't notice."

Q4 SAT-STYLE QUESTION Write a full answer to the exam question on p58. It should cover 1-2 sides of A4. Pretend you are in the exam, and write the answer in 30 minutes. Use the planning page you have done to help you. (30 marks)

Q5 a) When the 30 minutes are up, read through your answer and check the following things:

- ☐ **The article has a clear introduction and conclusion.**
- ☐ **The article is persuasive. It gives good reasons to support one point of view. It acknowledges other points of view exist and gives reasons why they are wrong.**
- ☐ **The structure of the article is signposted for the reader.**
- ☐ **The article is written in paragraphs.**
- ☐ **Interesting vocabulary and sentence structures are used.**
- ☐ **A range of punctuation is used correctly, e.g. commas, colons, semicolons.**
- ☐ **The spelling is good.**

b) Make any corrections to your answer neatly.

Just put a line through anything you want to change — don't use correction fluid.

The Short Writing Question

The Short Writing Question is worth 20 marks. You only have 30 minutes to plan and write your answer and you don't get a planning page to help you. Here's how to tackle it.

A Case of Mistaken Identity

Your local newspaper is running a story-writing competition for young people:

Young Writers' Story Competition

The theme of this year's competition is mistaken identity.
Write an imaginative story on this topic. You should write about:

- The characters who are mistaken for each other and why they're so alike
- Who mixes them up
- What the result of the mix-up is

The winning entry will be published in the Herald newspaper.

Write your entry to the competition. *20 marks including 4 marks for spelling*

Q1 Sketch out a grid like this and fill it in.

QUESTION	ANSWER
What is the purpose of this piece of writing?	
Who is going to read it?	
Write down three words which describe the tone you think the writing should have.	

Q2 a) Write down three things that the question tells you should be included in your story.

b) Use the three things you know should be included as a way to organise your planning. Write them out as headings on a piece of paper. Then spend 5 minutes brainstorming ideas and scribbling them down under the headings.

Q3 SAT-STYLE QUESTION Write a full answer to the question. It should cover just over a side of A4. Pretend you are in the exam, and write your answer in 25 minutes. Use the plan you have written to help you. (20 marks)

Q4 When you have finished writing, spend a couple of minutes reading through your work and correcting any mistakes.

The section's almost over... keep going... one more...

Don't be scared of writing longer pieces. Planning your answer is the key. If it helps, write down "purpose, tone, structure, paragraphs, interesting sentences" at the top of your plan.

Revision Questions

Q1 SAT-STYLE QUESTION

This is an example of a long writing question. It should take 45 minutes, **including** 15 minutes planning time. Copy out the planning page onto an A4 sheet of paper before you start.

Today's News: Accident at Sporting Event

Write an article for a broadsheet newspaper about an accident at a major sporting event. You should make your account believable, but you do not have to base it on facts.

You should include:

- a headline
- a description of what happened
- quotes from people who witnessed the accident
- information about action which is going to be taken to improve safety in the future

30 marks

Use this page to plan your work.

a headline for your article

what happened, when and where

quotes from people who were there

what's going to happen next

Q2 SAT-STYLE QUESTION

This is another example of a long writing question.
Copy out the planning page onto an A4 sheet before you start.

Dealing with Bullying in Schools

Your school is trying to tackle bullying.
They want pupils to produce a leaflet on the topic:

Calling All Students

We would like you to produce a leaflet about how students can deal with bullying. It should comment on the advantages and disadvantages of different actions students can take, e.g.

- talking to a teacher
- talking to a friend or parent
- avoiding or ignoring the bullies
- fighting or talking back to the bullies

Write the text for the leaflet.

30 marks

Use this page to plan your work.

words and phrases to begin and end your discussion

different ways to deal with bullying

advantages and disadvantages of each method

Q3 SAT-STYLE QUESTION

Here's an example of a short writing question. Do it in **30 minutes.**

No Shakespeare at Local Theatre

A local theatre has decided to stop putting on Shakespeare's plays.
This is an extract from a letter by an English teacher to the local newspaper:

The local theatre has completely failed to see two important points:

1. **Shakespeare's plays are not boring; they are filled with humour, suspense and drama.**
2. **Students in local schools studying the plays gain a lot from seeing them performed.**

As a Year 9 pupil, write a letter to the managing director of the local theatre, Marcus Straw, arguing that Shakespeare's plays should still be performed there. You don't need to include an address.

20 marks including 4 marks for spelling

Know Your Play

You have to know the story of your play and a few basics about all the characters. If you don't you'll be very stuck on the day of the SAT. Do these questions and learn the answers.

Q1 a) Write a one or two sentence summary of each **scene** in your play.

b) Write a one or two sentence summary of each **act** in your play.

You'll only have to write about certain bits of the play — these are your set scenes. If you don't know which scenes they are, then ask your teacher right now.

Q2 a) Write a detailed summary of your set scenes.

b) Draw a storyboard for each of your set scenes.

It doesn't have to be fine art — just draw matchstick figures. The point is to get a clear picture of who's talking to who and what they're doing.

Q3 Sketch out a grid like this and fill it in for all the characters that appear in your set scenes.

e.g.

Name	Job or title	Age	Appearance	Personality	Quotes
Juliet	Daughter of Lord and Lady Capulet	13	Noble and rich Very beautiful	Lovely but emotional	"O Romeo, Romeo, Wherefore art thou Romeo?"

Q4 Copy out the list of themes for the play you're studying. Write down as many quotes as you can from your set scenes that are linked to the themes.

ROMEO AND JULIET

- Forbidden love
- Family
- Honour
- Death
- Innocence
- Deception

THE TEMPEST

- Fate and justice
- Magic
- Freedom
- Betrayal
- Forgiveness

Q5 Write down a one sentence definition for each of these words. If you don't know the answer look it up in a dictionary and rewrite the definition in your own words.

a) act
b) scene
c) character
d) tragedy
e) comedy
f) history play
g) line
h) speech
i) phrase
j) prose
k) poetry
l) metre
m) exit
n) exeunt
o) aside

Understanding the Language

The hardest thing about Shakespeare is understanding the language. You can learn some of the tricky words in advance, but it's best if you know how to work out what odd words mean, too.

Q1 The words on the left pop up all the time in Shakespeare. Write each of them out next to their modern meanings from the box on the right.

Make sure you do all 12.

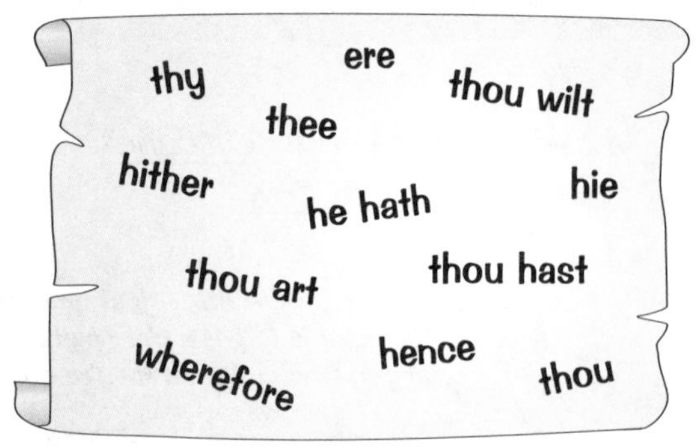

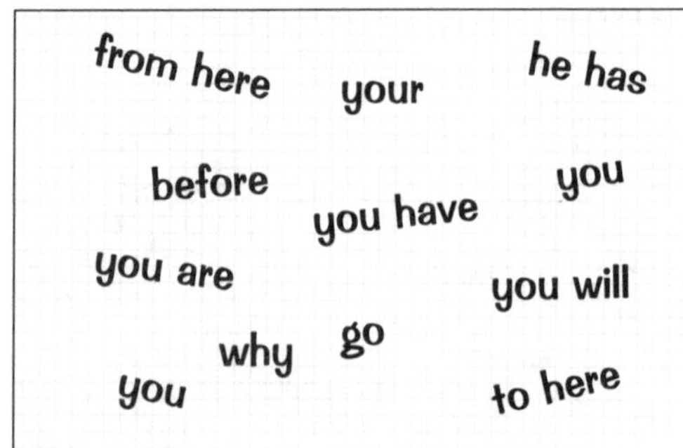

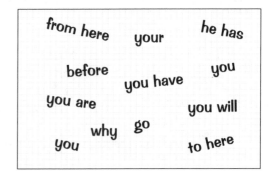

Q2 Write down what you think each highlighted word means.

Don't panic if you see a word you don't know — try and work it out.

a)

PARIS I do defy thy conjurations,
And apprehend thee for a felon here.

ROMEO Wilt thou provoke me? Then have at thee, boy!

***Romeo and Juliet*, Act 5 Scene 3, lines 68-70**

b)

PROSPERO O Ferdinand!
Do not smile at me that I boast her off,
For thou shalt find she will outstrip all praise,
And make it halt behind her.

***The Tempest*, Act 4 Scene 1, lines 8-11**

c)

CAPULET Go to, go to,
You are a saucy boy. Is't so indeed?
This trick may chance to scathe you, I know what.
You must contrary me! Marry, 'tis time.

***Romeo and Juliet*, Act 1 Scene 5, lines 81-84**

d)

SEBASTIAN 'Twas a sweet marriage, and we prosper well in our return.

ADRIAN Tunis was never graced before with such a paragon to their queen.

***The Tempest*, Act 2 Scene 1, lines 71-74**

Understanding the Language

If you've got a rough idea what the characters are going on about, you're doing pretty well. A good way to test whether you really understand is to put what they say into your own words.

Q1 Write this speech out in your own words.

ALONSO You cram these words into mine ears against
The stomach of my sense. Would I had never
Married my daughter there, for, coming thence,
My son is lost, and, in my rate, she too,
Who is so far from Italy removed
I ne'er shall see her. O thou mine heir
Of Naples and of Milan, what strange fish
Hath made his meal on thee?

***The Tempest*, Act 2 Scene 1, line 104-111**

Q2 Write this speech out in simple, modern language.

ROMEO Thou cans't not speak of that thou dost not feel:
Wert thou as young as I, Juliet thy love,
An hour but married, Tybalt murderèd,
Doting like me and like me banishèd,
Then mightst thou speak, then mightst thou tear thy hair,
And fall upon the ground, as I do now,
Taking the measure of an unmade grave.

***Romeo and Juliet*, Act 3 Scene 3, lines 64-70**

If there's a bit you don't get, have a guess at what it might mean.

Q3 You know what I'm going to say... Yep, write this speech out in your own words.

PROSPERO Behold, Sir King,
The wronged Duke of Milan, Prospero.
For more assurance that a living prince
Does now speak to thee, I embrace thy body,
And to thee and thy company I bid
A hearty welcome.

***The Tempest*, Act 5 Scene 1, lines 106-111**

Q4 Choose an extract from your set scenes that's at least 15 lines long. Write it out in your own words.

If you're still not sure which are your set scenes, then find out from your teacher now.

Backing Up Your Answers

You can have the world's brainiest ideas in your Shakespeare answer in the SAT, but you'll only get about half the marks if you don't back them up with quotes.

Q1 Look at each bit of text. Find the exact words which back up the statement on the right and write them down.

You don't need to explain your answers for now — just write out the bits of text you'll need.

a)

ROMEO I do protest I never injured thee,
But love thee better than thou canst devise,
Till thou shalt know the reason of my love;
And so, good Capulet, which name I tender
As dearly as mine own, be satisfied.

***Romeo and Juliet*, Act 3 Scene 1, lines 64-68**

Romeo loves the Capulets as much as he loves his own family.

There is one important phrase here.

b)

NURSE But first let me tell ye, if ye should lead her into a fool's paradise, as they say, it were a very gross kind of behaviour, as they say: for the gentlewoman is young; and, therefore, if you should deal double with her, truly it were an ill thing to be offered to any gentlewoman, and very weak dealing.

***Romeo and Juliet*, Act 2 Scene 4, lines 140-145**

The Nurse warns Romeo that cheating on Juliet would be nasty.

c)

PROSPERO For you, most wicked sir, whom to call brother
Would even infect my mouth, I do forgive
Thy rankest fault — all of them — and require
My dukedom of thee, which perforce I know
Thou must restore.

***The Tempest*, Act 5 Scene 1, lines 130-134**

Prospero should sound angry with Antonio, even though he forgives him.

These ones are a bit different. Imagine you've made these points, and try to back them up.

d)

JULIET Shall I speak ill of him that is my husband?
Ah, poor my lord, what tongue shall smooth thy name,
When I, thy three-hours wife, have mangled it?
But wherefore, villain, didst thou kill my cousin?
That villain cousin would have killed my husband.

***Romeo and Juliet*, Act 3 Scene 2, lines 97-101**

Juliet should sound angry with Romeo.

e)

PROSPERO you demi-puppets that
By moonshine do the green sour ringlets make,
Whereof the ewe not bites; and you whose pastime
Is to make midnight mushrooms, that rejoice
To hear the solemn curfew; by whose aid —
Weak masters though ye be — I have bedimmed
The noontide sun, called forth the mutinous winds,
And 'twixt the green sea and the azured vault
Set roaring war.

***The Tempest*, Act 5 Scene 1, lines 36-44**

Prospero shows how powerful his magic is by using lots of natural imagery.

You can't just quote one bit — you'll have to quote a few.

Backing Up Your Answers

... more practice at finding words from the text to prove your ideas are the product of full-blown genius.

Q1 Find the words in each piece of text which back up the statement to the right.

a)

FRIAR LAWRENCE The sun not yet thy sighs from heaven clears,
Thy old groans ring yet in my ancient ears.
Lo, here upon thy cheek the stain doth sit
Of an old tear that is not washed off yet.

***Romeo and Juliet*, Act 2 Scene 3, lines 73-76**

Friar Lawrence should point at Romeo's face here...

Find the words that suggest he sees something on Romeo's face.

b)

CALIBAN Why, as I told thee, 'tis a custom with him
I' th' afternoon to sleep. There thou mayst brain him,
Having first seized his books, or with a log
Batter his skull, or paunch him with a stake,
Or cut his wezand with thy knife. Remember
First to possess his books

***The Tempest*, Act 3 Scene 2, lines 87-92**

Caliban wants Prospero's death to be painful and violent.

Find the different ways that Caliban suggests Stephano should kill Prospero.

c)

MIRANDA Sir, are not you my father?

PROSPERO Thy mother was a piece of virtue, and
She said thou wast my daughter, and thy father
Was Duke of Milan, and his only heir
And princess, no worse issued.

MIRANDA O, the heavens!
What foul play had we that we came from thence?
Or blessed was't we did?

***The Tempest*, Act 1 Scene 2, lines 56-62**

Miranda is surprised to find out that she is the daughter of the Duke of Milan.

You need to look for an expression of surprise...

d)

ROMEO I must indeed, and therefore came I hither.
Good gentle youth, tempt not a desperate man.
Fly hence, and leave me: think upon these gone.
Let them affright thee. I beseech thee, youth,
Put not another sin upon my head,
By urging me to fury. O, be gone!
By heaven, I love thee better than myself,
For I come hither armed against myself.
Stay not, be gone; live, and hereafter say,
A madman's mercy bade thee run away.

***Romeo and Juliet*, Act 5 Scene 3, lines 58-67**

Romeo admits that he has done evil things in the past.

You can back this point up by saying that Romeo threatens Paris, showing he has an evil side.

Writing Your Answers

You make your point and you find a quote to back it up. Then you've got to explain how the quote backs up your comment. It shouldn't be too hard — just don't forget to do it.

Q1 *Here's something a bit easier to read as a break from all that Shakespeare.*

> **There once was a playwright called Kit**
> **Who wrote hit after hit after hit.**
> **Each day he used up forty goose-feather quills;**
> **Lords, ladies and gents all rated his skills —**
> **But the geese didn't like him one bit.**

a) Work through these questions, then put your answers together to give a full answer to the question in the box.

i) Was Kit's work successful in the theatre, yes or no?

ii) Which words tell you this?

iii) Explain why these words show the work was successful.

According to the limerick, was Kit's work popular?

b) Work through these questions, then put your answers together to give a full answer to the question in the box.

i) Which words tell you that people thought Kit was talented?

ii) What effects does the writer use, e.g. colourful adjectives, rhetorical question, repetition...?

iii) How do the effects that the writer uses add to the impression that people thought Kit talented?

How does the writer emphasise Kit's popularity?

c) Now answer this question fully, including your main point, a quote and an explanation.

Why didn't the geese like Kit?

Q2 Read this review and answer the question to the right. (6 marks)

SAT-STYLE QUESTION

> **Last night's performance of *The Tempest* was like a grand opera and a fireworks display rolled into one. Luke Matchett *lived* the role of Prospero and Frank Dunn's Caliban was suitably evil, whilst hinting at an underlying sadness. An absolute triumph!**

How does the writer emphasise her opinion about the performance?

Use parts a)-c) above to help you plan your answer. Back up your answer with quotes and explanations.

Writing Your Answers

You're on your own now, sunshine. Well, not quite alone. You've got all these lovely questions here to keep you company. Lucky you. Lucky, lucky, lucky you. Don't forget those quotes...

Q1 *Answer each question in turn. When you make a point, remember to back it up with a quote and explain how the point goes with your quote.*

JULIET What's in a name? That which we call a rose
By any other word would smell as sweet;
So Romeo would, were he not Romeo called,
Retain that dear perfection which he owes
Without that title. Romeo, doff thy name,
And for thy name, which is no part of thee,
Take all myself.

ROMEO I take thee at thy word.
Call me but love, and I'll be new baptised;
Henceforth I never will be Romeo.

JULIET What man art thou that thus bescreened in night
So stumblest on my counsel?

ROMEO By a name
I know not how to tell thee who I am.
My name, dear saint, is hateful to myself,
Because it is an enemy to thee;

***Romeo and Juliet*, Act 2 Scene 2, lines 43-56**

a) What impression does this extract give you of Romeo and Juliet's relationship?

b) Sketch out the grid below, then fill it in with quotes to back up each point.

Point	Quote
Names play an important part in Romeo and Juliet.	
Juliet would love Romeo if he abandoned his family.	
Romeo hates his name.	
Juliet wasn't expecting to hear Romeo.	

c) What kind of atmosphere is there in this scene?

Don't answer back — always answer forwards...

So, that's the basics of how to answer the questions. The next twenty pages or so are all about the different kinds of question you could get in the SAT. Twenty pages of unfettered joy. Sigh.

What Characters Do

When you get a 'character' question in the SATs — and you never know what you're going to get — the best place to start is by having a general look at what the characters do.

Q1 *This is what the main characters get up to in some early scenes of two Shakespeare plays.*

Romeo and Juliet — *ROMEO*

ACT 1 SCENE 1 Romeo is depressed because he loves a girl called Rosaline — who doesn't love him back.

ACT 1 SCENE 5 Romeo and his friends break into the Capulets' party to try and find some girls, which makes Tybalt angry. Romeo meets Juliet for the first time and it's love at first sight.

ACT 2 SCENE 2 Romeo climbs over the Capulets' wall to go and see Juliet. He declares his love for her.

Romeo and Juliet — *JULIET*

ACT 1 SCENE 3 Juliet is not interested in marrying Paris, even though he's rich and important.

ACT 1 SCENE 5 Juliet meets Romeo and they kiss. She finds out that he is a Montague and is devastated.

ACT 2 SCENE 2 Juliet talks about Romeo from her balcony. Romeo appears and they say they love each other.

The Tempest — *PROSPERO*

ACT 1 SCENE 2 Prospero tells Miranda he raised the storm with his magic. He is angry with Ariel when he complains about being given more work to do. Prospero threatens to torture Caliban if he doesn't do his tasks. Prospero is pleased when Miranda and Ferdinand fall in love but wants to test how strong their love is.

ACT 3 SCENE 1 Prospero is pleased as he sees how much Miranda and Ferdinand are in love.

a) Write out at least two of the words or phrases below to describe Romeo, Juliet and Prospero.

good with words **cheeky** **cunning** **romantic** **caring** **ruthless**
powerful **invincible** **has a temper** **useless** **has a good reputation**

b) Write a sentence to explain why you've chosen each word or phrase.

Q2 *Read this extract, then answer the questions.*

FRIAR LAWRENCE Hold, daughter, I do spy a kind of hope,
Which craves as desperate an execution
As that is desperate which we would prevent.
If, rather than to marry County Paris,
Thou hast the strength of will to slay thyself,
Then is it likely thou wilt undertake
A thing like death to chide away this shame,
That cop'st with Death himself to scape from it;
And if thou dar'st, I'll give thee remedy.

***Romeo and Juliet*, Act 4 Scene 1, lines 68-76**

a) Write these sentences out in the order of the speech above so they describe the Friar's plan.

"If you dare to do it, then I'll help." *"...then you'd be prepared to face death if it solved your problem."*

"I've thought of a plan, but it's dangerous." *"If you are strong enough to die rather than marry Paris..."*

b) Write a few sentences explaining what this extract tells you about Friar Lawrence's character.

What Characters Say

Almost everything a character says tells you a bit more about them.
Here's some more practice at working out what characters are like and writing about it.

Q1 *These extracts are both from speeches Caliban makes in* The Tempest.

A
This island's mine, by Sycorax my mother,
Which thou tak'st from me. When thou cam'st first,
Thou strok'st me and made much of me,
wouldst give me
Water with berries in't, and teach me how
To name the bigger light...

***The Tempest*, Act 1 Scene 2, lines 333-337**

Thou mak'st me merry. I am full of pleasure.
Let us be jocund — will you troll the catch
You taught me but whilere?

***The Tempest*, Act 3 Scene 2, lines 116-118**

a) Say which of the extracts each of these sentences is about.

Caliban says that he used to be treated better, and that rightfully the island is his.

Caliban wants to have a party.

b) Which speech shows Caliban thinks he owns the island? Explain why.

c) Which speech shows Caliban feels that he has been wronged? Explain why.

Q2 *These two bits are from speeches made by Prospero in* The Tempest.

A
A treacherous army levied, one midnight
Fated to th' purpose, did Antonio open
The gates of Milan, and i' th' dead of darkness,
The ministers for th' purpose hurried thence
Me and thy crying self.

***The Tempest*, Act 1 Scene 2, lines 129-133**

B
You, brother mine, that entertained ambition,
Expelled remorse and nature, who, with Sebastian —
Whose inward pinches therefore are most strong —
Would here have killed your king, I do forgive thee,
Unnatural though thou art.

***The Tempest*, Act 5 Scene 1, lines 75-79**

a) Say which of the extracts each of these sentences is about.

Prospero says he forgives Antonio and Sebastian for betraying him and plotting against Alonso.

Prospero talks about how he and Miranda were banished from Milan.

b) Write down three words you could use to describe Prospero as he appears in these quotes.

Q3 *These words are spoken by Romeo towards the end of* Romeo and Juliet.

A
How oft when men are at the point of death
Have they been merry! Which their keepers call
A lightning before death.

***Romeo and Juliet*, Act 5 Scene 3, lines 88-90**

Death, that hath sucked the honey of thy breath,
Hath had no power yet upon thy beauty.
Thou art not conquered.

***Romeo and Juliet*, Act 5 Scene 3, lines 92-94**

a) In your own words, write out what Romeo's saying in each speech.

b) Write down at least three words you could use to describe Romeo.

Just base your answer on these two extracts.

What Characters Say

For a really good 'character' answer you need to go into quite a bit of detail about the way the characters speak and how they treat each other.

You'll be able to answer the questions on this page even if you don't know the plays.

Q1 *Read the extract then answer the questions.*

King Alonso and his followers have just been washed up on an island after their ship was caught in a storm. Alonso fears his son Ferdinand is dead, but Gonzalo has been trying to comfort him.

ALONSO You cram these words into mine ears against
The stomach of my sense. Would I had never
Married my daughter there, for, coming thence,
My son is lost, and, in my rate, she too,
Who is so far from Italy removed
I ne'er again shall see her. O thou mine heir
Of Naples and of Milan, what strange fish
Hath made his meal on thee?

***The Tempest*, Act 2 Scene 1, lines 104-111**

a) Write out each of these comments about Alonso with the best explanation from the box.

i) Alonso is pessimistic.

ii) Alonso feels guilty.

iii) Alonso is irritable.

- **He's annoyed when people try to cheer him up.**
- **He blames himself for what's happened to Ferdinand.**
- **He feels sure Ferdinand is dead.**

b) Write down a quote from the extract to back up each of the explanations from part a).

Q2 *Read the extract then answer the questions.*

LADY CAPULET Well, well, thou hast a careful father, child,
One who, to put thee from thy heaviness,
Hath sorted out a sudden day of joy,
That thou expects not, nor I looked not for.

JULIET Madam, in happy time, what day is that?

LADY CAPULET Marry, my child, early next Thursday morn,
The gallant, young, and noble gentleman,
The County Paris, at Saint Peter's Church,
Shall happily make thee there a joyful bride.

JULIET Now by Saint Peter's Church and Peter too,
He shall not make me there a joyful bride.

***Romeo and Juliet*, Act 3 Scene 5, lines 107-117**

Juliet is refusing to marry Paris, even though her father has secretly arranged a wedding to surprise her.

a) Write out each of these comments about the characters' feelings and match with the best quote from the box.

i) Juliet has been feeling down recently.

ii) Lady Capulet is happily surprised.

iii) Juliet's dad has worked hard to get the wedding sorted quickly.

iv) Juliet feels reluctant to marry Paris.

- **"thou hast a careful father, child, / One who... / Hath sorted out a sudden day of joy"**
- **"to put thee from thy heaviness,"**
- **"He shall not make me there a joyful bride."**
- **"a sudden day of joy, / That thou expects not, nor I looked not for."**

What Characters Say

It's all about <u>backing up</u> your answer. You can say Benvolio and Mercutio were turquoise unicorns with an obsession with candyfloss — so long as you can back it up with evidence...

Q1 Read the piece of text, then sketch out the table and fill in the missing explanations and quotes.

FRIAR LAWRENCE What, rouse thee, man! Thy Juliet is alive,
For whose dear sake thou wast but lately dead;
There art thou happy. Tybalt would kill thee,
But thou slew'st Tybalt — there art thou happy.
The law that threatened death becomes thy friend,
And turns it to exile; there art thou happy:
A pack of blessings lights upon thy back.
Happiness courts thee in her best array,
But, like a misbehavèd and sullen wench,
Thou pout'st upon thy fortune and thy love:
Take heed, take heed, for such die miserable.

***Romeo and Juliet*, Act 3 Scene 3, lines 136-146**

Comment	Explanation	Quote
Romeo is ungrateful for all the luck he's had recently.	Friar Lawrence says that at least he and Juliet are both alive and well, and his life is saved.	"A pack of blessings lights upon thy back."
Romeo has been saved from execution even though he killed Tybalt.		
Romeo wanted to be dead for Juliet's sake.		

Q2 Read the extract below, then sketch a grid like the one from Q1 and fill in as many comments, backed up by quotes and explanations, as you can.

PROSPERO Thou poisonous slave, got by the devil himself
Upon thy wicked dam, come forth!

Enter CALIBAN

CALIBAN As wicked dew as e'er my mother brushed
With raven's feather from unwholesome fen
Drop on you both! A south-west blow on ye
And blister you all o'er!

PROSPERO For this, be sure, tonight thou shalt have cramps,
Side-stitches that shall pen thy breath up, urchins
Shall, for that vast of night that they may work,
All exercise on thee, thou shalt be pinched
As thick as honeycomb, each pinch more stinging
Than bees that made 'em.

CALIBAN I must eat my dinner.
This island's mine, by Sycorax my mother,
Which thou tak'st from me. When thou cam'st first,
Thou strok'st me and made much of me, wouldst give me
Water with berries in't, and teach me how
To name the bigger light, and how the less,
That burn by day and night, and then I loved thee,
And showed thee all the qualities o'th'isle,
The fresh springs, brine-pits, barren place and fertile.
Cursed be I that did so! All the charms
Of Sycorax, toads, beetles, bats, light on you!

***The Tempest*, Act 1 Scene 2, lines 321-342**

Q3 SAT-STYLE QUESTION Choose a character who's in all your set scenes. Write an essay explaining what we learn about the character in the scenes. (18 marks)

Don't forget to explain your points and back them up with quotes.

How Characters Think

For these questions you have to work out why the character acts a particular way.

Q1 *In this extract from* The Tempest, *Prospero gives his slave Caliban some instructions.*

PROSPERO Hag-seed, hence!
Fetch us in fuel. And be quick, thou 'rt best,
To answer other business. Shrugg'st thou, malice?
If thou neglect'st, or dost unwillingly
What I command, I'll rack thee with old cramps,
Fill all thy bones with aches, make thee roar,
That beasts shall tremble at thy din.
CALIBAN No, pray thee.
(aside) I must obey. His art is of such power,
It would control my dam's god, Setebos,
And make a vassal of him.

***The Tempest*, Act 1 Scene 2, lines 367-376**

rack = torture

art = magic

vassal = inferior person

a) What does Prospero tell Caliban to do?

b) Why does Prospero become annoyed with Caliban?

c) Why does Caliban decide to do as he is told?

Q2 Below are three quotes from Lord Capulet in *Romeo and Juliet*. Match each one to the correct summary.

A
I would not for the wealth of all this town
Here in my house do him disparagement;
Therefore be patient, take no note of him;
***Romeo and Juliet*, Act 1 Scene 5, lines 68-70**

B
My sword, I say! Old Montague is come,
And flourishes his blade in spite of me.
***Romeo and Juliet*, Act 1 Scene 1, lines 69-70**

C
Day, night, work, play,
Alone, in company, still my care hath been
To have her matched;
***Romeo and Juliet*, Act 3 Scene 5, lines 176-178**

i) Lord Capulet has been trying hard to find Juliet a husband.

ii) Lord Capulet doesn't want to kick Romeo out of the party.

iii) Lord Capulet wants to fight Lord Montague.

Q3 Read the extract from *The Tempest* then answer the questions below.

PROSPERO Thou most lying slave,
Whom stripes may move, not kindness! I have used thee,
Filth as thou art, with human care, and lodged thee
In mine own cell, till thou didst seek to violate
The honour of my child.

***The Tempest*, Act 1 Scene 2, lines 346-350**

Prospero is telling Caliban that he was treated with love and care until he tried to attack Miranda.

stripes = whips

a) What kind of words suggest Caliban is badly treated?

b) Why is Caliban no longer a friend of Prospero and Miranda?

Writing About Descriptions

You won't have to write a whole essay on description — but try to mention it in any language task.

Q1 *In this bit from* Romeo and Juliet, *Romeo talks about how he has had a dream that something bad is going to happen that evening.*

ROMEO I fear, too early, for my mind misgives
Some consequence yet hanging in the stars
Shall bitterly begin his fearful date
With this night's revels and expire the term
Of a despisèd life closed in my breast,
By some vile forfeit of untimely death.
But He, that hath the steerage of my course,
Direct my sail! On, lusty gentlemen.

***Romeo and Juliet*, Act 1 Scene 4, lines 106-113**

He = God

Some consequence hanging in the stars = fate

a) Write these lines out in the order they come in the scene.

Let's get going.

God's in charge of my life course, he'll do what he wants.

The party tonight will end badly.

Something big is going to happen tonight.

b) Write down two phrases which show Romeo's feelings about the party.

c) Write down one phrase which shows Romeo's attitude to fate.

d) What is Romeo's reaction to his dream — what does he decide to do about it?

e) Write a mini-essay explaining how the language of this piece creates a feeling of tension in the scene. Include information from your answers to a) to d). (8 marks)

SAT-STYLE QUESTION

Q2 Write a mini-essay explaining how the language in this bit from *Romeo and Juliet* creates a clear picture of the Montagues' and Capulets' past behaviour. (8 marks)

SAT-STYLE QUESTION

PRINCE Rebellious subjects, enemies to peace,
Profaners of this neighbour-stainèd steel —
Will they not hear? — What, ho! You men, you beasts!
That quench the fire of your pernicious rage
with purple fountains issuing from your veins,
On pain of torture, from those bloody hands
Throw your mistempered weapons to the ground,
And hear the sentence of your movèd prince.
Three civil brawls, bred of an airy word,
By thee, old Capulet, and Montague,
Have thrice disturbed the quiet of our streets,
And made Verona's ancient citizens
Cast by their grave beseeming ornaments,
To wield old partisans, in hands as old.

***Romeo and Juliet*, Act 1 Scene 1, lines 73-86**

Writing About Imagery

If you're writing about language and you spot some imagery, definitely mention it. It'll go down a treat with the examiners.

Q1 *For each extract below, answer the questions that follow.*

FRIAR LAWRENCE These violent delights have violent ends
And in their triumph die, like fire and powder.

***Romeo and Juliet*, Act 2 Scene 6, lines 9-10**

powder = gunpowder

fiddlestick= violin bow or sword
dance= dance or dodge

MERCUTIO And thou make minstrels of us, look to hear nothing but discords.
Here's my fiddlestick, here's that shall make you dance.

***Romeo and Juliet*, Act 3 Scene 1, lines 42-45**

Caliban, Stephano and Trinculo are driven out

PROSPERO Go charge my goblins that they grind their joints
With dry convulsions, shorten up their sinews
With aged cramps, and more pinch-spotted make them
Than pard or cat o' mountain.

***The Tempest*, Act 4 Scene 1, lines 257-260**

Prospero is telling Ariel to use magic to torment Caliban, Stephano and Trinculo, who have been plotting against Prospero.

pard = leopard

cat o' mountain = another word for leopard

a) What's being described in the image?

b) What's it being compared to?

c) What does the image tell you about the thing being described?

d) What does the image tell you about the character's thoughts or state of mind?

e) What does the image add to the overall feel of the play? Explain your answer.

It's OK if you only answer e) for the play you're studying.

Q2 SAT-STYLE QUESTION What effect do you think the imagery in this extract from *the Tempest* would have on an audience? Use parts a) to d) from above to help you plan your mini-essay. (8 marks)

Prospero was overthrown by Antonio as Duke of Milan. He and his daughter Miranda were dropped in the sea in a tiny, leaky boat and left to die. In this extract Prospero tells Miranda what happened.

PROSPERO In few, they hurried us aboard a bark,
Bore us some leagues to the sea, where they prepared
A rotten carcass of a butt, not rigged,
Nor tackle, sail, nor mast. The very rats
Instinctively have quit it. There they hoist us,
To cry to th'sea, that roared to us, to sigh
To th'winds, whose pity, sighing back again,
Did us but loving wrong.

***The Tempest*, Act 1 Scene 2, lines 145-152**

bark = a kind of boat

rigged, tackle = sailing terms

Writing About the Mood

Mood means the atmosphere the language creates and how it makes the audience feel.

Q1 Read the extracts, then sketch out and fill in the table below.

	Setting	How the characters speak	Description & imagery	MOOD
A				
B				

CALIBAN How does thy honour? Let me lick thy shoe.
I'll not serve him — he is not valiant.
TRINCULO Thou liest, most ignorant monster: I am in case to jostle a constable. Why, thou debauched fish, thou, was there ever man a coward that hath drunk so much sack as I today? Wilt thou tell a monstrous lie, being but half a fish and half a monster?
CALIBAN Lo, how he mocks me! Wilt thou let him, my lord?
TRINCULO 'Lord' quoth he! That a monster should be such a natural!
CALIBAN Lo, lo again! Bite him to death, I prithee.

***The Tempest*, Act 3 Scene 2, lines 22-30**

For each note you make, write a quote to show where you got your idea from.

natural = idiot

B

JULIET What devil art thou that dost torment me thus?
This torture should be roared in dismal hell.
Hath Romeo slain himself? Say thou but 'ay'
And that bare vowel 'I' shall poison more
Than the death-darting eye of cockatrice.
I am not I, if there be such an 'ay',
Or those eyes shut, that makes thee answer 'ay'.
If he be slain, say 'ay', or if not, 'no':
Brief sounds determine my weal or woe.

Romeo and Juliet, Act 3 Scene 2, lines 43-51

cockatrice = mythical creature which killed with a look.

weal = happiness

MERCUTIO Nay, I'll conjure too.
Romeo! Humours! Madman! Passion! Lover!
Appear thou in the likeness of a sigh,
Speak but one rhyme, and I am satisfied.
Cry but 'Ay me!' pronounce but 'love' and 'dove',
Speak to my gossip Venus one fair word,
One nickname for her purblind son and heir,
Young Adam Cupid, he that shot so trim,
When King Cophetua loved the beggar-maid!
He heareth not, he stirreth not, he moveth not;
The ape is dead, and I must conjure him.
I conjure thee by Rosaline's bright eyes,
By her high forehead and her scarlet lip,
By her fine foot, straight leg and quivering thigh
And the demesnes that there adjacent lie,
That in thy likeness thou appear to us!

***Romeo and Juliet*, Act 2 Scene 1, lines 6-21**

purblind = totally blind

demesnes = park land

SAT-STYLE QUESTION

Q2 Write a mini-essay on the mood in one of the extracts, using your notes from Q1. (8 marks)

Writing About Persuasive Language

Examiners love it when you write about persuasive language. Shakespeare uses lots of tricks you can look out for.

Q1 Write down a quote from the extract to show where each of the persuading tricks is being used.

Antonio is trying to persuade Sebastian to kill Alonso and Gonzalo so that Sebastian can take his place as King of Naples.

ANTONIO Twenty consciences
That stand 'twixt me and Milan, candied be they
And melt, ere they molest! Here lies your brother,
No better than the earth he lies upon,
If he were that which now he's like — that's dead —
Whom I with this obedient steel, three inches of it,
Can lay to bed for ever, whiles you, doing thus,
To the perpetual wink for aye might put
This ancient morsel, this Sir Prudence, who
Should not upbraid our course. For all the rest,
They'll take suggestion as a cat laps milk,
They'll tell the clock to any business that
We say befits the hour.

***The Tempest*, Act 2 Scene 1, lines 277-289**

Persuading tricks

says it will be very simple to kill Alonso

scoffs at the idea of feeling guilty

says Gonzalo won't be a problem

says no one else will stand in their way

Q2 Write down a quote from the extract to show where each of the persuading tricks is being used.

Juliet is telling the Nurse not to blame or hate Romeo, even though he has just killed Tybalt, Juliet's cousin, in a street fight.

NURSE Shame come to Romeo!
JULIET Blistered be thy tongue
For such a wish! He was not born to shame:
Upon his brow shame is ashamed to sit;
For 'tis a throne where honour may be crowned
Sole monarch of the universal earth.
O what a beast I was to chide at him!
NURSE Will you speak well of him that killed your cousin?
JULIET Shall I speak ill of him that is my husband?

***Romeo and Juliet*, Act 3 Scene 2, lines 90-97**

Persuading tricks

uses rhetorical questions

standing up to insults

uses violent language to emphasise her emotions

romantic language

insisting Romeo is honourable

Q3 Write a mini-essay on how persuasive tricks are used in one of the extracts above. (12 marks)

SAT-STYLE QUESTION

Art thou afeard o' the dreaded SAT?

Mentioning persuasive language in SAT questions will make the examiner as happy as an aardvark wearing ant-infested pants. Point out any persuasive bits and say <u>how</u> they persuade the audience.

Revision Questions — Romeo and Juliet

This page mixes up a few of the topics from this section.

How does the language add to the hostile atmosphere of these lines?

ROMEO — Villain I am none;
Therefore farewell, I see thou knowest me not.

TYBALT — Boy, this shall not excuse the injuries
That thou hast done me, therefore turn and draw.

ROMEO — I do protest I never injured thee,
But love thee better than thou canst devise,
Till thou shalt know the reason of my love;
And so, good Capulet, which name I tender
As dearly as mine own, be satisfied.

MERCUTIO — O calm, dishonourable, vile submission!
'Alla stoccata' carries it away. (*Draws*)
Tybalt, you rat-catcher, will you walk?

TYBALT — What wouldst thou have with me?

MERCUTIO — Good King of Cats, nothing but one of your nine lives that I mean to make bold withal, as you shall use me hereafter, dry-beat the rest of the eight. Will you pluck your sword out of his pilcher by the ears? Make haste, lest mine be about your ears ere it be out.

TYBALT — I am for you. (*Drawing*)

***Romeo and Juliet*, Act 3 Scene 1, lines 60-78**

Romeo tries to convince Tybalt not to fight him, but Tybalt won't listen. Mercutio decides to fight Tybalt instead.

Alla stoccata = a sword fighting phrase.

rat-catcher, King of Cats = in a popular story at the time, the King of Cats was called Tibalt.

Q1 a) Write down any words or phrases that look like they've got something to do with the question.

b) Looking at the extract, have a go at answering each of these questions. Don't forget to quote.

i) What do the different characters think and feel?
ii) Are there any descriptive bits? What effect do they have?
iii) Is there any imagery used? If so, what does it add to the passage?
iv) Are most of the sentences long or short?
v) Is the rhythm quick and choppy or slow and steady?

Ask yourself these things on any language question.

These two can have a big effect on how exciting / magical / confusing the atmosphere of a scene is.

c) Look back at your answers to a). If you haven't got a comment for each of the quotes, think about how it links to the question now, and write it down.

d) Plan a full answer to the question at the top of the page, using your answers to a) - c).

e) Use all your notes to write out a full answer to the question at the top of the page. (18 marks)

SAT-STYLE QUESTION

Revision Questions — The Tempest

Two more big fat questions. Use parts a) to d) from page 79 to break them up into nicer chunks.

Q1 How does the language in this extract create a mood of mystery and magic? (18 marks)

SAT-STYLE QUESTION

Prospero is about to cast one final spell before he gives up his magic.

PROSPERO *(drawing a magic circle on the ground)*
Ye elves of hills, brooks, standing lakes, and groves;
And ye that on the sands with printless foot
Do chase the ebbing Neptune, and do fly him
When he comes back; you demi-puppets that
By moonshine do the green sour ringlets make,
Whereof the ewe not bites; and you whose pastime
Is to make midnight mushrooms, that rejoice
To hear the solemn curfew; by whose aid —
Weak masters though ye be — I have bedimmed
The noontide sun, called forth the mutinous winds,
And 'twixt the green sea and the azured vault
Set roaring war. To the dread rattling thunder
Have I given fire, and rifted Jove's stout oak
With his own bolt; the strong-based promontory
Have I made shake, and by the spurs plucked up
The pine and cedar. Graves at my command
Have waked their sleepers, oped, and let 'em forth,
By my so potent art. But this rough magic
I here abjure, and, when I have required
Some heavenly music — which even now I do —
To work mine end upon their senses that
This airy charm is for, I'll break my staff,
Bury it certain fathoms in the earth,
And deeper than did ever plummet sound
I'll drown my book.

***The Tempest*, Act 5 Scene 1, lines 33-57**

Neptune = God of the Sea

demi-puppets = fairies

azured vault = blue sky, heaven

promontory = cliff

abjure = give up

Q2 How does the language in this extract show the closeness and yet also the distance in Prospero's relationship with his daughter? (18 marks)

SAT-STYLE QUESTION

Prospero wants more for his daughter and begins to tell her about her past.

perdition= disaster

bootless= pointless

PROSPERO No harm.
I have done nothing but in care of thee,
Of thee, my dear one, thee, my daughter, who
Art ignorant of what thou art, nought knowing
Of whence I am, nor that I am more better
Than Prospero, master of a full poor cell,
And thy no greater father.

MIRANDA More to know
Did never meddle with my thoughts.

PROSPERO 'Tis time
I should inform thee farther. Lend thy hand,
And pluck my magic garment from me. So,
Lie there my art. Wipe thou thine eyes. Have comfort.
The direful spectacle of the wreck, which touched
The very virtue of compassion in thee,
I have with such provision in mine art
So safely ordered that there is no soul —
No, not so much perdition as an hair,
Betid to any creature in the vessel
Which thou heard'st cry, which thou saw'st sink. Sit down,
For thou must now know farther.

MIRANDA You have often
Begun to tell me what I am, but stopped,
And left me to a bootless inquisition,
Concluding 'Stay, not yet.'

PROSPERO The hour's now come,
The very minute bids thee open thine ear.
Obey, and be attentive.

Name a smoothie playwright — milkshakespeare...

Like a good ice-cream sundae, language questions are usually a bit of a mix. Think about all the topics in this section if you're writing about language. And strawberry sauce. And nuts. Mmm.

Performance — The Basics

For 'performance' questions you normally have to imagine you're the director of the scene. They want you to show that you understand what's going on in the scene and how it could look on stage.

Q1 a) Copy out all the bits here where Prospero's talking to himself.

Always ask yourself exactly who the characters are speaking to.

PROSPERO Soft, sir, one word more!
(Aside) They are both in either's pow'rs, but this swift business
I must uneasy make, lest too light winning
Make the prize light. *(To Ferdinand)* One word more — I charge thee
That thou attend me — thou dost here usurp
The name thou ow'st not and hast put thyself
Upon this island as a spy, to win it
From me, the lord on't.

***The Tempest*, Act 1 Scene 2, lines 452-459**

Prospero's decided to make things difficult for Ferdinand and Miranda, in order to test their love for each other.

Hi! I'm actor and heartthrob Sam Panda. You may remember me from such films as 'Star Trip: Live long and Prospero' and 'Romeo-cop'.

b) Which of the words on the right describes the way Prospero might talk when he's talking to himself?

c) Which of the words on the right describes the way Prospero might talk when he's talking to Ferdinand?

thoughtful forceful loud
angry
accusatory quiet

Q2 *Characters' feelings often change **during** a scene. Read this extract and look out for changes.*

ROMEO I must indeed, and therefore came I hither.
Good gentle youth, tempt not a desperate man.
Fly hence, and leave me: think upon these gone.
Let them affright thee. I beseech thee, youth,
Put not another sin upon my head,
By urging me to fury. O, be gone!
By heaven, I love thee better than myself,
For I came hither armed against myself.
Stay not, be gone; live, and hereafter say,
A madman's mercy bade thee run away.

PARIS I do defy thy conjurations,
And apprehend thee for a felon here.

ROMEO Will thou provoke me? Then have at thee, boy!

***Romeo and Juliet*, Act 5 Scene 3, lines 58-70**

Explain how and why Romeo's feelings change during this extract.

How Characters Speak

The Number 1 Big Thing to include in 'imagine you're a director' questions is how the characters should sound — what tone of voice they should use, how loudly they speak — that sort of thing.

Q1a) Say how you think the speaker feels and what they are thinking in each of the highlighted parts of the text.

There's no right or wrong answer to this question.

LADY CAPULET He is a kinsman to the Montague,
Affection makes him false, he speaks not true:
Some twenty of them fought in this black strife,
And all those twenty could but kill one life.
I beg for justice, which thou, Prince, must give:
Romeo slew Tybalt, Romeo must not live.
PRINCE Romeo slew him, he slew Mercutio;
Who now the price of his dear blood doth owe?
MONTAGUE Not Romeo, Prince, he was Mercutio's friend;
His fault concludes but what the law should end,
The life of Tybalt.

PRINCE And for that offence
Immediately we do exile him hence.
I have an interest in your hearts' proceeding;
My blood for your rude brawls doth lie a-bleeding;
But I'll amerce you with so strong a fine
That you shall all repent the loss of mine.
I will be deaf to pleading and excuses,
No tears nor prayers shall purchase out abuses.
Therefore use none. Let Romeo hence in haste,
Else, when he is found, that hour is his last.
Bear hence this body, and attend our will:
Mercy but murders, pardoning those that kill.

***Romeo and Juliet*, Act 3 Scene 1, lines 171-192**

b) Suggest what tone of voice each actor could use to emphasise emotions to the audience when they speak the highlighted words. Choose from the suggestions below, or use your own ideas.

annoyed **worried** **single-minded** **angry** **commanding** **determined**
remorseless **assertive** **confident** **impatient** **regretful**

Q2 SAT-STYLE QUESTION Suggest how the actor playing Prospero could speak the lines below to emphasise his feelings to the audience. (12 marks)

PROSPERO O good Gonzalo,
My true preserver, and a loyal sir
To him thou follow'st! I will pay thy graces
Home both in word and deed. Most cruelly
Didst thou, Alonso, use me and my daughter.
Thy brother was a furtherer in the act. —
Thou art pinched for't now, Sebastian. — Flesh and blood,
You, brother mine, that entertained ambition,
Expelled remorse and nature, who, with Sebastian —
Whose inward pinches therefore are most strong —
Would here have killed your king, I do forgive thee,
Unnatural though thou art. Their understanding
Begins to swell, and the approaching tide
Will shortly fill the reasonable shore
That now lies foul and muddy. Not one of them
That yet looks on me, or would know me. Ariel,
Fetch me the hat and rapier in my cell.

***The Tempest*, Act 5 Scene 1, lines 68-84**

Detailed answers get good marks. General wishy-washy ones get zilch marks.

rapier = a type of sword

How Characters Move

The second Big Thing to include in 'imagine you're a director' questions is how the characters should move. Movements can emphasise what the characters say and how they react to other characters.

Q1 *Read the extract on the right and answer the questions.*

a) Write out all the bits that tell you how the characters should move and describe the movements in your own words.

b) Write down other possible movements — quote to show **when** the characters should move.

PROSPERO The fringed curtains of thine eye advance,
And say what thou seest yond.
MIRANDA What is't? A spirit?
Lord, how it looks about! Believe me, sir,
It carries a brave form. But 'tis a spirit.
PROSPERO No, wench — it eats and sleeps and hath such senses
As we have, such. This gallant which thou seest
Was in the wreck, and but he's something stained
With grief, that's beauty's canker, thou mightst call him
A goodly person. He hath lost his fellows,
And strays about to find 'em.

***The Tempest*, Act 1 Scene 2, lines 411-420**

Q2 Write down your ideas for how each of the characters could speak and move in these lines.

JULIET Good pilgrim, you do wrong your hand too much,
Which mannerly devotion shows in this,
For saints have hands that pilgrims' hands do touch,
And palm to palm is holy palmers' kiss.
ROMEO Have not saints lips, and holy palmers too?
JULIET Ay, pilgrim, lips that they must use in prayer.
ROMEO O then, dear saint, let lips do what hands do:
They pray — grant thou, lest faith turn to despair.
JULIET Saints do not move, though grant for prayers' sake.
ROMEO Then move not while my prayer's effect I take.
Thus from my lips, by thine, my sin is purged.
Kissing her

***Romeo and Juliet*, Act 1 Scene 5, lines 96-106**

Romeo is chatting up Juliet at the Capulet family party.

Q3 Write down any bits in the following extract where characters could emphasise their feelings through their movements, and suggest what those movements could be.

PROSPERO *(Aside)* I had forgot that foul conspiracy
Of the beast Caliban and his confederates
Against my life. The minute of their plot
Is almost come. *(To the spirits)* Well done! Avoid — no more!
(the spirits depart)
FERDINAND This is strange. Your father's in some passion
That works him strongly.
MIRANDA Never till this day
Saw I him touched with anger so distempered.

***The Tempest*, Act 4 Scene 1, lines 139-145**

Subtle face movements? No problem.

Prospero has just remembered Caliban's plot against him and broken off the masque to celebrate Ferdinand and Miranda's engagement.

In this extract the movements are probably going to be quite subtle. Think about facial expressions as well as big movements.

Revision Questions — Romeo and Juliet

After you've answered parts a) to b) you can tackle the SAT question below. In the SAT you'll have to write about two separate bits from the play and they'll be quite a lot longer, but this is great practice.

Imagine you are directing this extract from *Romeo and Juliet* for a class performance. Explain how the actors should play their parts.

ROMEO Let me be tane, let me be put to death,
I am content, so thou wilt have it so.
I'll say yon grey is not the morning's eye,
'Tis but the pale reflex of Cynthia's brow;
Nor that is not the lark whose notes do beat
The vaulty heaven so high above our heads.
I have more care to stay than will to go:
Come, death, and welcome! Juliet wills it so.
How is't, my soul? Let's talk, it is not day.

JULIET It is, it is, hie hence, be gone, away!
It is the lark that sings so out of tune,
Straining harsh discords and unpleasing sharps.
Some say the lark makes sweet division:
This doth not so, for she divideth us.
Some say the lark and loathèd toad changed eyes;
O now I would they had changed voices too,
Since arm from arm that voice doth us affray,
Hunting thee hence with hunt's-up to the day.
O now be gone, more light and light it grows.
ROMEO More light and light, more dark and dark our woes!

Enter NURSE (hastily)

NURSE Madam!
JULIET Nurse?
NURSE Your lady mother is coming to your chamber.
The day is broke, be wary, look about.

Exit.

***Romeo and Juliet*, Act 3 Scene 5, lines 17-40**

Romeo is in Juliet's bedroom. He has been exiled so he has to leave before it gets light but says he would like to stay. Juliet begs him to go or he will be killed.

Q1 a) I've stuck dotted lines onto the text to break it into chunks. Describe briefly what is said in each chunk.

b) Write each of the characters' names at the top of a page. Under each heading answer these questions, covering one chunk of the extract at a time.

i) Who is the character talking to?
ii) How does the character feel? Back this up with a quote.
iii) What movements can the actor use to show how the character feels?
iv) What tone of voice can the actor use to show how the character feels?
v) Should any words get extra emphasis from the actor's movements or tone of voice?

Say how they feel when they're speaking AND listening.

c) Decide what order to cover your points in and write an answer to the question at the top of the page. (18 marks)

SAT-STYLE QUESTION

You could write about one character at a time, or follow the order of the extract.

Revision Questions — The Tempest

Two more monster questions. Use part b) from page 84 to break them into bitesize bits.

Q1 SAT-STYLE QUESTION

Imagine you are directing *The Tempest*. Explain how the actor playing Ariel should show his feelings in these lines from the play. (18 marks)

Prospero wants to put on a show for Miranda and Ferdinand.

PROSPERO Sit, then, and talk with her, she is thine own.
What, Ariel! My industrious servant, Ariel!

Enter ARIEL

ARIEL What would my potent master? Here I am.

PROSPERO Thou and thy meaner fellows your last service
Did worthily perform, and I must use you
In such another trick. Go bring the rabble,
O'er whom I gave thee pow'r, here to this place.
Incite them to quick motion, for I must
Bestow upon the eyes of this young couple
Some vanity of mine art — it is my promise,
And they expect it from me.

ARIEL Presently?

PROSPERO Ay, with a twink.

ARIEL Before you can say 'come' and 'go',
And breathe twice, and cry 'so, so',
Each one, tripping on his toe,
Will be here with mop and mow.
Do you love me, master? No?

PROSPERO Dearly, my delicate Ariel. Do not approach
Till thou dost hear me call.

ARIEL Well! I conceive.

Exit

***The Tempest*, Act 4 Scene 1, lines 32-50**

Q2 SAT-STYLE QUESTION

Imagine you are directing this extract from *The Tempest*. Write instructions for the actors, concentrating on their movements and tone of voice. (18 marks)

Trinculo has just come across Caliban while looking for shelter.

TRINCULO Warm, o' my troth! I do now let loose my opinion, hold it no longer — this is no fish, but an islander, that hath lately suffered by a thunderbolt. *(thunder)* Alas, the storm is come again! My best way is to creep under his gaberdine, there is no other shelter hereabout. Misery acquaints a man with strange bed-fellows. I will here shroud till the dregs of the storm be past.

Enter STEPHANO *singing, a bottle in his hand*

STEPHANO *(sings)* I shall no more to sea, to sea,
Here shall I die ashore —
This is a very scurvy tune to sing at a man's funeral.
Well, here's my comfort. *(drinks and sings)*
The master, the swabber, the boatswain, and I,
The gunner, and his mate,
Loved Mall, Meg, and Marian, and Margery,
But none of us cared for Kate,
For she had a tongue with a tang,
Would cry to a sailor 'Go hang!'
She loved not the savour of tar nor of pitch,
Yet a tailor might scratch her where'er she did itch.
Then to sea, boys, and let her go hang!
This is a scurvy tune too, but here's my comfort. *(drinks)*

CALIBAN Do not torment me. O!

STEPHANO What's the matter? Have we devils here? Do you put tricks upon's with savages and men of Ind? Ha! I have not scaped drowning to be afeard now of your four legs, for it hath been said, 'As proper a man as ever went on four legs cannot make him give ground,' and it shall be said so again, while Stephano breathes at nostrils.

CALIBAN The spirit torments me. O!

***The Tempest*, Act 2 Scene 2, lines 33-62**

Julie-ate her copy of the Shakespeare play...

Examiners always prefer it if you answer the exact question. If you don't they turn into slavering beasts. If they ask you to concentrate on movements, feelings or tone of voice, make sure you do.

Ideas, Themes and Issues in Romeo and Juliet

The themes of a play are the big ideas that the play's about. If you get asked to write about themes in the SAT, you'll have to say how a certain bit of text relates to the main theme.

Q1 Juliet is more concerned with love than with family loyalty.
Answer all of the questions below about the themes in this extract.

JULIET 'Tis but thy name that is my enemy —
Thou art thyself, though not a Montague.
What's Montague? It is nor hand nor foot,
Nor arm nor face, nor any other part
Belonging to a man. O be some other name!
What's in a name? That which we call a rose
By any other word would smell as sweet;
So Romeo would, were he not Romeo called,
Retain that dear perfection which he owes
Without that title. Romeo, doff thy name,
And for thy name, which is no part of thee,
Take all myself.

***Romeo and Juliet*, Act 2 Scene 2, lines 38-49**

doff = take off

a) Write out all the parts of the speech that mention names.

b) Write down what each one means.

c) In your opinion, what does Juliet think about names?

d) What do you think Shakespeare is telling the audience about names in this speech?

Q2 (SAT-STYLE QUESTION) What different ideas about life and death does Shakespeare present in the speech below? Ask yourself questions like a)-d) above to help you plan your answer. (18 marks)

ROMEO What less than doomsday is the Prince's doom?

LAWRENCE A gentler judgement vanished from his lips,
Not body's death, but body's banishment.

ROMEO Ha, banishment! Be merciful, say 'death';
For exile hath more terror in his look,
Much more than death. Do not say 'banishment'.

LAWRENCE Hence from Verona art thou banishèd:
Be patient, for the world is broad and wide.

ROMEO There is no world without Verona walls,
But purgatory, torture, hell itself.
Hence 'banishèd' is banished from the world,
And world's exile is death: then banishèd
Is death mistermed. Calling death 'banishèd',
Thou cut'st my head off with a golden axe,
And smilest upon the stroke that murders me.

***Romeo and Juliet*, Act 3 Scene 3, lines 9-23**

Ideas, Themes and Issues in The Tempest

**The Tempest is all about fate, justice and forgiveness.
You might get a SAT question asking you how the extract shows one of these main themes.**

Q1 *One of the main themes of* The Tempest *is justice.*

ARIEL you three
From Milan did supplant good Prospero,
Exposed unto the sea, which hath requit it,
Him, and his innocent child, for which foul deed
The pow'rs, delaying, not forgetting, have
Incensed the seas and shores, yea, all the creatures,
Against your peace. Thee of thy son, Alonso,
They have bereft, and do pronounce by me
Ling'ring perdition, worse than any death
Can be at once, shall step by step attend
You and your ways, whose wraths to guard you from —
Which here, in this most desolate isle, else falls
Upon your heads — is nothing but heart's sorrow,
And a clear life ensuing.

***The Tempest*, Act 3 Scene 3, lines 69-82**

requit = avenged

bereft = deprived, taken

perdition = loss, ruin

a) Write out all the parts of the speech that are about justice.

b) Write down what each one means in your own words.

c) Write down what you think Ariel is saying about justice.

d) What do you think Shakespeare thinks about justice?

Q2 SAT-STYLE QUESTION What different ideas about forgiveness does Shakespeare present in the speech below? Ask yourself questions like a)-d) above to help you plan your answer. (18 marks)

ARIEL Him you termed, sir, 'the good old lord, Gonzalo'.
His tears run down his beard, like winter's drops
From eaves of reeds. Your charm so strongly works 'em
That if you now beheld them your affections
Would become tender.

PROSPERO Dost thou think so, spirit?

ARIEL Mine would, sir, were I human.

PROSPERO And mine shall.
Hast thou, which art but air, a touch, a feeling
Of their afflictions, and shall not myself,
One of their kind, that relish all as sharply,
Passion as they, be kindlier moved than thou art?
Though with their high wrongs I am struck to th' quick,
Yet with my nobler reason 'gainst my fury
Do I take part. The rarer action is
In virtue than in vengeance. They being penitent,
The sole drift of my purpose doth extend
Not a frown further. Go release them, Ariel.
My charms I'll break, their senses I'll restore,
And they shall be themselves.

***The Tempest*, Act 5 Scene 1, lines 15-32**

Ideas, Themes and Issues

Q1 *Another key idea in* Romeo and Juliet *is hatred and the feud between the two families.*

SAMPSON Draw, if you be men. Gregory,
remember thy washing blow.
They fight
BENVOLIO Part, fools!
Put up your swords — you know not what you do.
Beats down their swords
Enter TYBALT
TYBALT What, art thou drawn among these heartless hinds?
Turn thee, Benvolio, look upon thy death.
BENVOLIO I do but keep the peace. Put up thy sword,
Or manage it to part these men with me.
TYBALT What, drawn, and talk of peace! I hate the word,
As I hate hell, all Montagues, and thee:
Have at thee, coward!
They fight
Enter several of both houses, who join the fray.
Then enter three or four CITIZENS with clubs
FIRST CITIZEN Clubs, bills, and partisans!
Strike! Beat them down! Down with the
Capulets! Down with the Montagues!

***Romeo and Juliet*, Act 1 Scene 1, lines 54-66**

washing = slashing

hinds = female deer

clubs, bills, and partisans = types of weapon

a) Write out all the parts of this extract that make reference to hatred and feud between the two families.

b) Write down what each one means in your own words.

c) Write down what you think Tybalt's attitude towards the Montagues is.

d) What do you think Shakespeare is telling us about the feud in this extract?

Q2 SAT-STYLE QUESTION What different ideas about the struggle for power between masters and servants does Shakespeare present in the passage below? Ask yourself questions like a)-d) above to help you plan your answer. (18 marks)

CALIBAN I must eat my dinner.
This island's mine, by Sycorax my mother,
Which thou tak'st from me. When thou cam'st first,
Thou strok'st me and made much of me, wouldst give me
Water with berries in't, and teach me how
To name the bigger light, and how the less,
That burn by day and night, and then I loved thee,
And showed thee all the qualities o' th' isle,
The fresh springs, brine-pits, barren place and fertile.
Cursed be I that did so! All the charms
Of Sycorax, toads, beetles, bats, light on you!
For I am all the subjects that you have,
Which first was mine own king, and here you sty me
In this hard rock, whiles you do keep from me
The rest o' th' island.
PROSPERO Thou most lying slave,
Whom stripes may move, not kindness! I have used thee,
Filth as thou art, with human care, and lodged thee
In mine own cell

***The Tempest*, Act 1 Scene 2, lines 332-349**

Thou strok'st me and made much of me = You took care of me

Teach me how / To name the bigger light, and how the less= taught me about the sun and the moon

sty me = keep me

stripes = strikes with a whip

Answers

Reading Answers

Reading — The Basics

Page 2 Finding Facts

Q1

Description	Fact
Year PB Animation Studio was created	1998
Founded by...	Paul Black
Paul Black's current position	Managing Director
Total number of employees today	230

Q2 20 centimetres

Q3 wire frames (or armatures)

Q4 rod-and-joint structures

Q5 iii) 24

Q6 In order for the characters' movements to appear realistic on-screen.

Q7 The quality of its 3-D animation.

Page 3 Finding the Important Bits

Q1 a) Carrie darted round the corner into a dingy side street full of discarded wooden crates.

b) ...followed by Ben, who stopped and bent over, panting.
He felt like he'd been out of breath ever since...

c) ...ever since they'd left the Pirate Academy.

d) ...the leering, cruel face of Captain Hack.

e) ...must walk the plank.

f) ...any student failing to hand in homework...

g) Ben dashed forward with a yell, and managed to slip between Captain Hack's legs.

h) Ben ripped a thin plank of wood from a nearby crate.

Q2 Suddenly they were aware of a shadow looming over them.

Q3 She's about to use it as a sword against Captain Hack. The part of the text is: "Then she remembered her sword-fighting lessons, and crouched with the plank in her hand, ready to defend herself against her pirate tutor."

Page 4 Backing Up Points

Q1 Hanif strongly dislikes the rabbits and wants to get rid of them.

Q2 iii) Hanif wants to get rid of the rabbits. He calls them 'stinking', which shows that he doesn't like them.

Q3 i) Hanif has a strong opinion about the rabbits.

Q4 Milla is nervous.

Q5 Milla glanced around the street nervously

Q6 ii) Milla seems to be worried that someone will see her dumping the envelope into the bin.

Q7 Miles says that he'll be fine, but the fact that there is 'a hint of a tear in his eye' shows that he's not fine at all, and he's just being brave about his feelings.

Page 5 Summarising

Q1 The king, Felix, the king's courtier, Prime Minister Katan, two attendants (and the captured knights and the dragon for extra points!)

Q2 The king and Felix

Q3 The king remembers when his father was king, and knights were **easier** to control. **He starts to think about his childhood when he played with toys in the garden**. Then he decides that something must be done about the knights.

Q4 ii) He seems angry with Felix, but is easily distracted by memories of his childhood.

Q5 The king accuses Felix of failing to stop the knights from escaping. He tells Prime Minister Katan to tie Felix up, take him to Vertis Ledge, and leave him to the dragons.

Q6 The king is angry because all of his captured knights have escaped. He reminisces about when his father was king and his own childhood. He blames Felix for allowing the knights to escape. He instructs the Prime Minister to tie Felix up and leave him to the dragons on Vertis Ledge. As Felix is taken away, he threatens the king.

Page 6 Different Types of Text

Q1 Epilepsy — The Facts — A
Using your T-300 — D
Waiting — B
A man alone — C

Q2 A and D

Q3 B and C

Q4 Poem — B
Story — C
Manual — D
Magazine article — A

Q5 a) D

b) B

c) A

d) C

Reading — Working Things Out

Page 7 Working Out What's Going On

Q1

Event	Order in extract
Looks for tickets	2
Puts milk bottles outside	5
Wakes up	1
Has an accident in the kitchen	3
Puts front doors keys with tickets	4

Q2 • without them she *definitely* wouldn't be going on holiday today.

Q3 • before sacrificing two of the dishes to the floor in a flurry of ceramic and congealed Chinese takeaway.

Q4 ii) Mrs Hanrahan knocked over two dirty dishes, and they smashed on the floor.

Q5 The front door locks behind her.

Q6 *Any sensible answer is OK, e.g.:*
Mrs Hanrahan won't be able to get back into the house because the front door has locked and she left the keys inside. She won't be able to get the tickets, so she won't be able to go on holiday.

Reading Answers

Page 8 Working Out What's Going On

Q1 Using automatic cameras rather than manual cameras, and not developing the films yourself.

Q2 Film speed — "'Slow' films are suitable for normal lighting, whereas you'll need to use a faster ISO 400 film to take pictures on gloomy days (or as fast as ISO 1000 if it's night-time)."

Q3 ISO 100, because the text says that ISO 400 is fast and ISO 1000 is even faster.

Q4 The next issue of the magazine will feature an article about developing pictures in a darkroom.

Q5

Camera setting	Set to...	Reason
Film speed	ISO 400	Bright light
Aperture setting	Narrow	Bright light
Shutter speed	Short	Detailed action shots

Q6

Camera setting	Set to...	Reason
Film speed	ISO 1000	In the dark
Aperture setting	Wide	In the dark
Shutter speed	Long	Blurry pictures

Q7 • The writer says that automatic cameras are easier because you just have to 'point, press, and get someone else to do the dirty work'.
• You have to think about the type of film to use.
• You have to work out aperture settings.
• You have to think about shutter speed.
• You usually have to do the focusing yourself.
• You may have to develop the pictures yourself in a darkroom.
This question is like the kind of thing you get in the SAT. If you mention any 5 of the things above, you should get 5 marks.

Page 9 Working Out How Characters Feel

Q1 • towards Camelot and the King he had wished never to see again

Q2 i) Lancelot wishes he was free to go where he wanted and didn't have to walk any more.

Q3 • trudge grimly
• hack his way wearily

Q4 • if only to be finally at peace
Lancelot is so tired that even being dead sounds pleasant because then he could rest.

Q5 • Had to cut through dense foliage — Tired and frustrated
• Waded through rivers and walked in wet clothes — Uncomfortable
• Killed many other knights — Sad because he respected them

Q6 Points that could be made:
• Lancelot would be mentally and physically exhausted
• He would be moving very slowly by then
• He would be uncomfortable
• He wouldn't want to see the King
• He would be upset at having killed other knights

Reading — The Way It's Written

Page 10 Descriptions

Q1

Thing being described	How it's described
The whole city	Peaceful
The light from the lamp	Flickering
The doorway	Narrow
The dogs guarding the doorway	Snarling
The sheet of paper	Faded and yellow
Inspector Graham's hand	Trembling
The inside of the room	Dim

Q2 • flickering lamplight
• snarling dogs
• trembling hand
• dim inside of the room

Q3 • a small stone carving of a man crouching as if about to pounce at the Inspector

Q4 iii) The statue is described as if it is alive — this effect is called personification.

Q5 • The river flowed gently past the houses as if it didn't want to wake up the slumbering inhabitants

Q6 • The writer builds up suspense by describing the quiet city.
• Inspector Graham expects trouble at any moment
• Inspector Graham is nervous — his hand trembles
• The night before Graham had come across snarling dogs guarding the doorway
• The door creaks open, which sounds scary
• The lamplight flickers and the room is very dim
• The stone carving is described as if it is alive and about to attack the Inspector
This question is like the kind you'll get in the SAT. Any 5 of the things above would get you 5 marks.

Page 11 Descriptions of Characters

Q1 ii) Sarah seems to feel sorry for David and tries to keep him happy.

Q2 • surveyed him with a slightly pitying look
• Sarah tried to keep smiling, but failed

Q3 David — short-tempered, stressed
Sarah — sympathetic, tolerant
Denise — arrogant, stunning

Reading Answers

Q4 David — short-tempered:
- He wheeled around abruptly
- He grabbed Sarah by the lapels of her smart jacket
- "And *where* is our leading lady?" demanded David

David — stressed:
- asked David in a shaky voice
- he started to pull at the few tufts of greying hair left on his head
- his eyes darting from side to side as if following the path of a wasp

Sarah — sympathetic, tolerant
- surveyed him with a slightly pitying look
- Sarah tried to keep smiling, but failed

Denise — arrogant:
- "Your ravishing, immensely talented leading lady has just entered the building,"
- A figure sauntered casually into the light
- She tossed back her mane of honey-coloured hair
- fixed David with a commanding gaze

Denise — stunning:
- said a silky voice
- She tossed back her mane of honey-coloured hair
- Denise continued in a steady, alluring tone

Q5
- The fact that Denise tosses her hair makes her sound confident and arrogant
- Denise's hair is described as a mane, which makes her sound like a lion, which is a very impressive, aggressive and proud animal
- Denise's hair is described as honey-coloured, which makes it sound very pretty but maybe a bit sickly too

Q6 The fact that Denise saunters into the room makes her sound very confident and arrogant

Q7
- David is tired and nervous, which contrasts with Sarah, who is described as 'fresh-faced'
- David is very nervous, which contrasts with Denise, who saunters into the room and has a 'commanding gaze'
- Sarah tries to be kind to David, which contrasts with Denise, who seems to look down at David

This question is like the kind you'll get in the SAT. If you mentioned the last 3 points, backed up with your answers to Q3 and Q4, you'd get 5 marks.

Page 12 Similes and Metaphors

Q1 a) neither
b) simile
c) metaphor

Q2 ii) The shouting audience sounded noisy and tuneless, like wolf howls.

Q3 simile

Q4

Thing being described	Description the writer uses	Simile or metaphor	What this means
Leo Ryder	he was a monster	metaphor	he was angry and impressive
Arnie X playing guitar	possessed by the ghost of Jimi Hendrix	metaphor	he played as well as Jimi Hendrix
Jay Bryson beating the drums	as if they were fires to be put out	simile	he looked panicked
	he managed to keep time as faithfully as an honest referee	simile	he kept time very well

Page 13 Mood

Q1 A — tense
B — sad
C — happy

Q2 No. She watches her friends open their envelopes first, and then opens hers very slowly:
- Her fingers tugged gently at the envelope

Q3 The word 'weep' makes it sound as if the ceilings are crying and upset, just like the family after the dog died

Q4 It shows that Daniel is happy, because it makes him sound like an animal without any worries

Q5 i) They slow the pace down before Rachel opens the envelope, which builds up suspense.

Q6 B — the phrase 'long, pale faces' sounds very sad

Q7 It shows that the family are sad about the dog — they don't speak very much or make eye contact. The phrase makes the whole text seem very sad.

Pages 14/15 Long Language Question

Q1
- rounded bodies
- new and ghastly looking creatures
- in shape somewhat resembling an octopus
- with huge and very long and flexible tentacles
- The skin had a glistening texture, unpleasant to see, like shiny leather
- They were the size of a fair-sized swine
- the tentacles seemed to be many feet in length

Q2

Any picture that looks a bit like this is fine.

Q3 Adjectives:
i) wave-worn
ii) horrible
iii) ghastly
v) flexible
vi) glistening
ix) revolting

Adverbs:
iv) copiously
vii) flatly
viii) intensely
x) slowly

Q4 ii) The skin had a glistening texture, unpleasant to see, like shiny leather.

Q5
- it does not appear that Mr Fison was afraid, or that he realised that he was in any danger
- he was horrified, of course, and intensely excited and indignant

Q6
- large intelligent eyes
- gave the creatures a grotesque suggestion of a face
- their eyes regarded him with evil interest
- making a soft purring sound to each other

Q7
- The rounded bodies fell apart
- slowly uncoiling their tentacles
- creeping at first deliberately

Reading Answers

Q8 iii) Very slowly — Builds up suspense

Q9 • The writer describes the creatures as 'ghastly looking'
• The writer uses the simile that the creatures' skin had a 'glistening texture, unpleasant to see, like shiny leather', which makes them sound very ugly.
• The creatures move slowly, which builds up suspense and makes the creatures seem more menacing.
• The writer says that Mr Fison is 'horrified' at seeing the creatures.
• The writer uses personification in phrases like 'their eyes regarded him with evil interest' to show that the creatures are intelligent, which makes them seem more horrific.
This question is very like the kind you'll get in the SAT. If you make 5 points similar to the ones above, you should get 10 marks.

Page 16 Layout

Q1 A diary or journal — each entry is dated, and the language is abbreviated and informal.

Q2 To show when things happened, and to point out the start of each entry.

Q3 ii) To make the article feel like a conversation between the writer and the reader.

Q4 To make the text easier to follow, and to make it easy to refer back to points quickly.

Q5 Extra tips and explanations of the information in the list.

Q6 They link each tip to the correct numbered point.

Page 17 Structure

Q1 • It draws the reader in because it points out that the reader won't have heard of Alexis Bright, but soon he will be very famous.
• The reader will want to know why Alexis Bright will become famous.

Q2 The writer explains what kind of book 'A Tale of Two Celebrities' is, and what happens in the book.

Q3 • The first paragraph introduces Alexis Bright and the second paragraph tells you what the review is about.
• After reading the first paragraph, the reader will want to know what Alexis Bright has done that will make him famous.

Q4 • The third paragraph explains why some people will like the book, and why it will be a big seller
• The fourth paragraph explains why some people won't like the book

Q5 To contrast the two different opinions that people will have about the book.

Q6 i) The last sentence refers back to the introduction and sums up the main point of the review.

Q7 *If you mention your answers to questions 1, 3, 5 and 6 you'll get your 10 marks.*

Reading — The Writer's Viewpoint

Page 18 Persuading the Reader

Q1 To make the reader buy Bonza Biscuits

Q2 • luxury biscuit treat
• Not only are they tasty, they're great value too
• the most satisfying chocolate biscuits you'll ever have

Q3

Body part	Description
legs	like tree trunks
forehead	damp
hands	pudgy and clay-like
eyes	narrow and squinting
nose	peeling

Q4 iii) Mr Blister is a really ugly and unpleasant man

Q5 • The writer does not want the reader to like Mr Blister.
• He is described as very ugly (with 'peeling nose' and 'damp forehead'), which makes him sound unpleasant to look at.
• Also, the writer says that Mr Blister thinks of people as 'idiots' that 'made him feel ill', which makes him sound very mean too.
If you mention the three points above (but you could use different examples to back them up) then you'll get your 3 marks.

Page 19 Changes in the Writer's Opinion

Q1 i) My parents saw it as an educational experience

Q2 The writer goes backstage at Jackson's Travelling Circus, and doesn't like what she sees

Q3 The third paragraph

Q4 Unfortunately, the reality of the circus was far less exotic than I had previously believed

Q5 The sight of the elephants pacing sadly up and down brought tears to my eyes

Q6 • The answer is wrong because the writer used to love circuses, but now she thinks they're a bit cruel. The question mark in the title wouldn't back up that answer anyway.
• A better answer would be: The writer added a question mark to the title 'All The Fun of the Fair?' to show that she used to believe that circuses were great, but now she's not so sure.

Q7 *If you mention your answers to questions 1-6 you'll get your 5 marks.*

Page 20 The Effect on the Reader

Q1 The narrator is a criminal. He and his gang have been trying to rob a safe, and the criminal thinks that his partners have all been captured.

Q2 • Wouldn't you?

Q3 ii) It sounds as if the character is talking to you and it involves you in the decision.

Q4 iii) The writer wants to make the reader feel like they're actually taking part in the story.

Q5 • you and I know that there would have been no point
• surely you don't think I was unreasonable

Reading Answers

Q6 • The writer asks the reader to 'imagine the situation', which encourages them to become involved in the story.
• The writer uses rhetorical questions to make the reader feel as if they're involved in the main character's decisions.
• The main character addresses the reader directly in phrases like 'you and I know', which makes the reader feel that they know the main character.
If you mention any three points like the ones above then you'll get 5 marks.

Reading — Comparing Texts

Page 21/22/23 Comparing Texts

Q1 *The Macaque Monkeys of Japan* — Diary
I, Monkey — Story
Monkey Behaviour — Magazine article

Q2 • they're excited and buzzing around like annoying flies

Q3 • they're excited and buzzing around like annoying flies
• the cheek of it!
• maybe have a chat about the weather

Q4 • It worked!
Many phrases contain abbreviated language too, such as:
• Macaque monkeys currently living in the centre of the island

Q5 • To make the text easier to follow
• To divide the text up into days because it is a diary

Q6 i) Macaque monkeys currently living in the centre of the island

Q7 ii) The monkey is more intelligent than the scientists realise. The monkey tells the story from his point of view, which shows the scientists are wrong.

Q8 i) The writer thinks that humans are not ruled by instinct, but that all animals and insects are.

Q9 ii) All three texts are about whether the behaviour of monkeys is purely instinctive.

Q10

Name of extract	The Macaque Monkeys of Japan	I, Monkey	Monkey Behaviour
Is the extract fiction or non-fiction?	non-fiction	fiction	non-fiction
Is descriptive language used?	No	Yes	No
Is the language formal or informal?	Informal	Informal	Formal
Is there a first-person narrator?	Yes	Yes	No
Does the writer use facts to back up their points?	Yes	No	Yes
Does the writer think that animals are ruled by instinct?	No	No	Yes

Q11 • *The Macaque Monkeys of Japan* is broken up into the days that things are happening. This makes the text easy to follow and it also shows where each new day begins.
• *The Macaque Monkeys of Japan* was written one day at a time, so the structure just follows the order that things happened.
• *I, Monkey* is laid out in long paragraphs.
• *I, Monkey* starts with the monkey explaining what has happened, and ends with him saying that he plans to escape.
If you mention any three of the points above, you'll get 3 marks.

Q12 • *I, Monkey* uses informal language.
• *I, Monkey* uses humour in phrases like 'the cheek of it!'
• *Monkey Behaviour* uses formal language.
• There is no humour in *Monkey Behaviour.*
If you mention any three of the points above, you'll get 3 marks.

Q13 • The writer of *The Macaque Monkeys of Japan* is trying to prove that the behaviour patterns of monkeys can change.
• By the end of the *The Macaque Monkeys of Japan* the writer feels he has proved that monkeys are not ruled by instinct.
• The writer of *Monkey Behaviour* thinks that all animals and insects are purely ruled by instinct.
• The writer of *Monkey Behaviour* believes that only humans are not purely ruled by instinct.
If you mention any three of the points above, you'll get 3 marks.

Reading — Revision Questions

Page 24/25 Answers Without Prompts

Q1 Wilde writes that 'a sharp pang of pain struck like a knife across him', and this **simile** shows that Dorian feels physically hurt when he realises that he will grow old. Later, Dorian **panics** when Wilde writes that 'he felt as if a hand of ice had been laid upon his heart'.

Q2 • How does Hallward feel about his painting?
• How does Lord Henry react to seeing the painting?
• What do the characters say to Dorian before and after seeing the painting?

Q3 • The first two prompts ask how Lord Henry and Hallward feel about each other, but the question asks about how they feel about **Dorian**.
• The third prompt asks about what Dorian thinks about the painting, but the question asks about how **Lord Henry** and **Basil Hallward** act.

Q4 • How does the language make the reader feel about old age?
• Which phrases describe Dorian's body when he is old?
• Does Oscar Wilde use similes and metaphors in the extract?

Q5 *Any reasonable set of three prompts, for example:*
• How does Dorian feel about old age at the beginning of the extract?
• What happens to change Dorian's opinion of old age?
• How does Dorian feel about old age at the end of the extract?

Reading Answers

Q6 i) Dorian isn't really aware of his beauty and doesn't believe the nice things that people say.

Q7 • Basil Hallward's compliments had seemed to him to be merely the charming exaggerations of friendship.
• He had listened to them, laughed at them, forgotten them.
• They had not influenced his nature.
• The sense of his own beauty came on him like a revelation.

Q8 He sees Hallward's painting of himself.

Q9 ii) Dorian realises that he is as beautiful as people have been telling him.

Q10 • The sense of his own beauty came on him like a revelation.

Q11 Dorian imagines when his face is 'wrinkled and wizen' and he feels so horrified that the thought hurts 'like a **knife** across him'. He imagines when 'the scarlet would pass away from his lips', which shows that he thinks that he will become **ugly**.

Q12 Dorian wishes that the portrait could grow old instead of him, so that he can always stay the same age.

Q13 *Any three reasonable prompts, for example:*
• How does Dorian feel about himself at the start of the extract?
• What happens to make Dorian change his opinion of himself?
• How does Dorian feel about his appearance afterwards?
• How does Dorian feel about growing old?
• What does Dorian wish for at the end of the extract?

Q14 • At the beginning of the extract Dorian doesn't believe people when they say that he is beautiful.
• Dorian's opinion of himself changes as soon as he sees the portrait of himself.
• When Dorian sees the portrait, he realises that he is as beautiful as people have said.
• Dorian imagines when he is old, and hates the idea.
• At the end of the extract Dorian wishes that he will never grow old.
This question is very like the kind you might get in the SAT. If you mention the five points above, you'll get 5 marks.

Page 26/27 Proper SAT Reading Questions

Q1 Uruguay

Q2

Description of fact	Number
Year of first World Cup final	1930
Largest stadium audience	200,000
Year Football Association was created	1963
Total viewing figures of 1998 World Cup	33.4 billion
Year Charles Miller took football to Brazil	1894
Number of teams playing in first World Cup Final	13
Year World Cup match sparked a war	1969

Q3 China — 5000 years ago

Q4 El Salvador and Honduras

Q5 Jules Rimet

Q6 Paris

Q7 • It's a joke
• The history actually goes back a very long time — about 5000 years

Q8 • The simile makes the fans sound crazy
• The fans sound like a big pack of fierce animals

Q9 • The metaphor makes the football games sound like battles
• It makes it sound as if there are no rules and people might get hurt

Q10 • To show that there are three separate ideas about why football is popular
• To make it easy to follow the text and to refer back to the points

Q11 • To make the reader feel like it's a conversation between themselves and the writer
• To show what each paragraph is about, and the question that each paragraph addresses

Q12 • It doesn't explain that the text is about the World Cup until the end of the first paragraph, which encourages the reader to keep reading to find out what's going on
• The first paragraph starts by putting the reader in the middle of the action, which is quite exciting
• The writer uses a simile ('snarling like hyenas') to make the description exciting
• The writer uses humour in the phrase 'this is not a scene from *Braveheart*', which might entertain the reader
Any three of the points above will get you 3 marks.

Q13

Subsection	Summary
Introduction	Tells you what the article is about and the first World Cup
'Where did football come from?'	The origins of football and how the rules were formed
'Is it really the beautiful game?'	The ways that football has been responsible for bad things
'What's so great about football?'	The popularity of football, and reasons why it is popular
'Who are the biggest football fans?'	The most football-mad fans and the 2002 World Cup

Q14 *Any reasonable summary, for example:*
The article explains the history of football and the World Cup. It describes some good and bad things that football has caused. It tries to explain why it is so popular and finishes by discussing the 2002 World Cup.

Q15 • it hasn't all been good
• these idiots continue to spoil the game for many other people

Q16 • He brought two footballs to Brazil
• He introduced football to Brazil

Q17 • The 'shrill blast' is the referee's whistle
• The ''thunk' of leather against leather' is the sound of a football being kicked by footballers wearing boots

Q18 • The rules are simple
• It doesn't take much organising to start a game
• There are often very dramatic incidents in the games

Q19 *Any reasonable answer, for example:*
• The ending talks about something that the reader will know about - i.e. the 2002 World Cup
• The writer talks about himself, saying that he also got caught up in the excitement - this makes the ending more personal
• The article ends with a bit of humour, when the writer says that he still doesn't understand the offside rule

Reading Answers

Q20 *Any reasonable answer, for example:*
- The writer thinks that football is exciting (he compares a match to a scene from *Braveheart* in the first paragraph)
- The writer knows that football is popular - he says it's the 'game we know and love'
- The writer doesn't like people spoiling football - he calls football hooligans 'idiots'
- He says that he got caught up in the national excitement surrounding the 2002 World Cup
- He doesn't really understand football completely - he says he doesn't understand the offside rule

Each of the points above will get you one mark, up to a maximum of 5 marks.

Q21
- The writer uses a popular reference in the phrase 'this is not a scene from *Braveheart'* in the first paragraph, which will entertain the reader
- The writer says that the World Cup is more serious than *Braveheart* in the first paragraph, which makes it sound a lot more important than it really is
- The writer says that 'The history of football goes back ever so slightly further than 1930', which is funny because football is about 5000 years old - this makes the reader feel that the article isn't just about dry facts and figures
- The writer compares Medieval football to a battlefield, which is funny because it shows the reader how different football used to be
- The article ends with humour, when the writer says that he still doesn't understand the offside rule - this makes the reader laugh at the end of the article and shows that the article was supposed to be fun

Each of the points above will get you one mark, up to a maximum of 5 marks.

Q22 *Any reasonable answers, for example:*
- The writer shows that football can be scary in the first paragraph, when he compares football fans to snarling hyenas
- The writer shows that the history of football hasn't been all nice, such as the Italians using a head as a ball
- The writer implies that Charles Miller introducing football to Brazil was a good thing, because now Brazil is 'the home of the most beautifully-played football in the world'
- The writer says that football hooligans 'spoil the game', and he calls them 'idiots'
- The writer says that even he got caught up in the national excitement, so he seems to believe that it's good that everyone gets excited about the same thing

Any five points like the ones above will get you 5 marks.

Writing Answers

Writing — Grammar, Vocabulary and Spelling

Page 28 Sentences, Phrases and Clauses

Q1 a) no full stop
b) no verb
c) no full stop
d) no verb
e) no subject, e.g. "he"
f) no capital letter at the beginning, no full stop
g) no verb
h) no subject, e.g. "he"
i) no verb

Q2 a) phrase
b) clause
c) main clause
d) clause
e) phrase
f) main clause
g) phrase
h) main clause
i) phrase

Q3 a) Before the start of term, I'll have to cram in lots of fun.
b) In the Atlantic ocean, you can see fish swimming.
c) In his best Western movies, Gary Cooper's acting was impressive.
d) Without a bit of mustard, this recipe tastes disgusting.
e) Without a doubt, porridge is better than gruel.
f) Very well then, I'll fight you for it.
g) In a desperate attempt at humour, Kim threw the egg against the wall.
h) Up in the attic, my brother tried to poison a rat.

Page 29 Commas, Semicolons and Colons

Q1 a) Walking beside the miniature poodle, Harley felt very tall indeed.
b) Helen pitied the spider in the sink, which was about to die.
c) Scurrying out of the way of the headmistress, Dana looked a bit sheepish.
d) He walked and talked, half an hour afterwards his head was cut off.

Q2 a) After the storm was over, my sister returned to the ranch.
b) Despite everything, I still had a soft spot for her.
c) He marched away from the station, without a single look back.
d) Way back, many centuries ago, not long after the Bible began, Jacob lived in the land of Canaan, a fine example of a family man.
e) Although the weather was hot, Abigail decided to wear a big jumper and corduroy jeans.

Q3 a) I'll tell you how I managed it: I walked up to him and asked him.
b) All I want from my hamster is: companionship, devotion and a small but tasty meal.
c) As my grandmother says: "Don't fight with your Grandad or I'll get you."
d) You should bring the following things: an inflatable dinghy, a life jacket and a foghorn.
e) Pigeons have been known to communicate as follows: "eeuak, eak, ouawk, ek-ek, ooch."

Q4 a) The star required: a trailer with a jacuzzi; three servants including a manicurist; a separate dog kennel and Scottish salmon sandwiches without crusts.
b) The footballer had it all: a strong left foot; a good eye for the ball; a lightning pace and nerves of steel.
c) He walked into the room; he had never been inside before.
d) Jim had made a huge pile; he owned a large percentage of the Nile.

Page 30 Apostrophes

Q1 a) Our son might not be perfect, but theirs is atrocious.
b) There's a small cat which lives in our barn.
c) It's sunny outside, why stay indoors?
d) The driver wanted the car repaired because its gearbox was making funny noises.
e) I really like the theatre; there's a good one in my home town.
f) <u>It's</u> is used correctly.
g) "It's a Wonderful Life" is a film with Jimmy Stewart. It's shown every Christmas.

Q2 a) The ostriches' beaks were all shiny.
b) My brother Alex's band are playing in the pub on Saturday.
c) She gave him her mum's favourite handkerchief, realising too late that it was covered in snot.
d) The children's section of the menu was uninspiring.
e) Elmer McCurdy's body was used as a fairground attraction for seventy years before people realised it was human and gave him a proper burial.
f) Marcus's piano was six feet tall; he couldn't reach the pedals.

Q3 a) I don't want to trouble you, but your Alsatian is in my garage.
b) The boxer won't fight without his lucky rabbit's foot.
c) Don't you think it's strange how television stars get thinner every year?
d) It's the best piece of music I've ever heard.
e) It isn't that unusual for people to have two part-time jobs.
f) I can't go to the gym. I won't go to the gym. I don't want to go to the gym.

Page 31 Speech, Question and Exclamation Marks

Q1 a) When asked if he was a communist, Ring Lardner Jr. replied, "I could tell you but I would hate myself in the morning."
c) Bette Davis said the famous line, "Fasten your seat belts, it's going to be a bumpy night," in the film 'All About Eve'.
d) When Tony Blair got into power, he kept saying, "Education, education, education."
b) and e) don't need speech marks.

Writing Answers

Q2 Jake burst through the door of the garage shop.
"Freeze!" he shouted. He was scared; he could feel the sweat rolling down his forehead and flooding his eyes. He moved towards the cashier, holding the bag out in one hand, grasping his fake gun in the other.
"Oh my life!" said the cashier, "Jake Smithson, what are you doing?" Jake stopped in his tracks. He had been told that a pair of tights over the head would render any human being unrecognisable. Maybe 15 denier wasn't enough.
"I'm not Jake Smithson," he said, backing away.
"Yes you are, I used to serve you lunch at St Hilda's Primary School. Fancy that! What are you getting up to these days?" she said. Quietly, she pressed the police alarm under the counter.

Q3 a) "I'm hard to get," said Slim, "all you have to do is ask."

b) "My name is Maximus Decimus Meridus," said the stranger, "and I will have my vengeance in this life or the next."

c) "I think I'm falling in love with her," said Fritz.
"Oh, I am sorry," said Brian.
"So am I," said Fritz.

d) "She was awfully decent about that cheese," said Caldicott.
"But I see she didn't leave much of the pickles," said Charters.

e) "I demand that you pay me one million dollars," said Dr Evil.

f) "You say you're alone but your table's set for four," said the policeman.
"That's nothing," the man replied, "my alarm clock's set for eight."

Page 32 Writing Interesting Sentences

Q1 a) Jim ran to the station because he needed to catch the last train.

b) I am prepared to wait until the governor decides what will happen.

c) Sergei Bubka thinks he is the best pole-vaulter in the world but I am better.

d) I was about to go shopping when the letter landed on the mat.

e) My ceramic frog collection is terrific and it's worth a lot of money too.

Q2 a) Isabel had only got one ticket. She didn't want to give it away.

b) Pancakes with sugar and lemon are good. Jam filling is also nice.

c) Daria flew over the wall. She landed in a heap at the bottom of the ditch.

d) St Malo is really hot in the summer. You can go swimming in the sea.

e) Una was going to miss the plane. Perhaps she could grab a lift on the boy's skateboard.

Q3 a) Don't we all know that paint dries slowly?

b) Surely we all know that the governor will be back next year?

c) Surely you're not saying that Muriel's lying?

d) Cybil didn't know where to look; hadn't that man left five days ago?

Q4 *e.g.*
Rita Hayworth was born in 1918 in America. Her family were Spanish and her original name was Margarita Cansino. From the age of 13 she danced in a stage act with her father. She spent a lot of time practising her dancing, which meant she missed out on most of her education. In the late 1930s, she started to get small roles in films. However, the American film industry was xenophobic and didn't like the fact that she looked Spanish. Her appearance was therefore changed in the following ways: her black hair was dyed red and her hairline was made higher by electrolysis. In addition to this, her Spanish-sounding name was changed to Rita Hayworth.

Page 33 Writing Interesting Sentences

Q1 a) Even though it was raining, I dashed to the supermarket.

b) It didn't matter if the police caught me any more; I had to stop running.

c) In the autumn, I will go on a fantastic holiday to Iceland.

d) "Please go away," I said.

e) Suddenly worried, I opened the satchel.

Q2 *e.g.*

a) drove

b) hurried

c) flew

d) trudged

e) ambled

Q3 a) he

b) it

c) They

d) she, him

e) She, him

Q4 *Possible answer:*
Frantz Fanon was born in the French colony of Martinique. <u>He</u> trained as a psychologist in France. <u>He</u> encountered racism <u>there</u>. <u>He</u> then decided to move to Algeria, which was a French colony. During his time <u>there</u>, he worked at a hospital.
Frantz Fanon supported the Algerian revolution against French colonial rule which started in 1954. <u>It</u> was very bitter and violent. In his role as a psychologist, Frantz Fanon treated both French soldiers who had tortured Algerian revolutionaries, and the victims of torture. <u>He</u> wrote a book about the revolution, called 'A Dying Colonialism'. <u>It</u> is very good.

Page 34 Writing Interesting Sentences

Q1 a) active

i) passive

b) passive

ii) active

c) active

iii) passive

d) passive

iv) active

Writing Answers

Q2 a) Be quiet in the museum.

b) Don't smoke in the flammable wigwam.

c) Try eating the frosted peas.

d) Go down to the dock of the bay.

Q3

What Leo said to John in the pub last night	How likely is it that Leo will buy the beer?
"I should buy some of your homemade beer."	he feels he ought to buy it, but it isn't definite that he will
"I might buy some of your homemade beer."	it's possible he will buy the beer
"If I was richer, I would buy your homemade beer."	he won't buy the beer
"I will buy some of your homemade beer"	he'll definitely buy the beer
"I can buy your homemade beer."	he is able to buy it, but it isn't definite that he will

Page 35 Vocabulary

Q1 *Possible answers (the nouns have been underlined):*

a) The cautious <u>boy</u> was scared that the ravenous <u>dog</u> would attack him.

b) Long-distance <u>swimming</u> is good <u>exercise</u>.

c) Poor <u>Orpheus</u> knew that he shouldn't look, but the overwhelming <u>temptation</u> to see his beloved <u>wife</u> was too much.

d) A gigantic <u>wave</u> came towards the little <u>shore</u> and drenched the unsuspecting <u>sunbathers</u>.

e) In the play <u>park</u> near my beautiful <u>house</u> there is an ancient <u>oak tree</u>.

f) I didn't know until that terrible <u>moment</u> how I would cope in such a challenging <u>situation</u>.

g) It was three long <u>days</u> before they realised that the intrepid <u>hamster</u> had escaped.

h) "It is a well-known <u>fact</u> that gorgeous <u>Robert Mitchum</u> is a brilliant <u>actor</u>," said my <u>mum</u>.

Q2 a) Maria turned to Emma and whispered, "I think we should be quiet, no one else is talking in here."

b) Maria turned to Emma and bellowed, "Get out of my sight, you ungrateful, horrible woman."

c) Maria turned to Emma and warbled, "The hills are alive with the sound of music."

d) Maria turned to Emma and groaned, "Not another gas bill."

e) Maria turned to Emma and griped, "All the other waitresses get better tips than me."

Q3 *Possible answers (the verbs have been underlined):*

a) Jane warmly <u>welcomed</u> the professor.

b) The captain <u>shouted</u> menacingly at his daughter.

c) I <u>walked</u> slowly down to the riverbank.

d) The cat <u>eyed</u> the salmon hungrily.

e) "Surely not the Maltese Falcon!" said Sam excitedly.

f) The robber was <u>caught</u> dramatically in the street.

g) The mastermind <u>paced</u> thoughtfully up and down the dank room.

Page 36 Vocabulary

Q1 *Possible answer:*

	The girl was <u>nice</u>.	The play was <u>interesting</u>.	The results were <u>bad</u>.	She's <u>good</u> at the piano.	The sea captain was <u>old</u>.
informal word	friendly	watchable	awful	fantastic	ancient
formal word	pleasant	engrossing	unfortunate	talented	elderly

Q2 *Possible answers:*

a) invaded, really annoying, for starters, squawk, can't hear yourself think, let alone, plus, poo

b) The pigeons, which started living in the church steeple two months ago, are causing disruption. For example, they make a lot of noise, distracting people and drowning out the sound of the choir. Also, we have to put up with bird excrement in the choir stalls. It really is too much to bear.

Q3 Adjectives: blue, quiet, old, quiet, awful
Adverbs: slowly, very much, slowly, quickly
Possible answer (adjectives and adverbs have been underlined):

Paul walked <u>timidly</u> down to the dock. The <u>mysterious</u> boat was still there, docked at the end of the <u>gloomy</u> jetty. He hoped <u>feverishly</u> that the man had gone. There was a storm gathering <u>rapidly</u> overhead. He realised <u>suddenly</u> that it had grown dark. He took off his shoes and climbed onto the deck. There was the <u>familiar</u> door, with the scorch marks from the fire still there. From beyond the door he heard a <u>crackling</u> voice:

"Come in my child. You are welcome here."

Paul was struck by a <u>paralysing</u> fear. He knew that voice.

Page 37 Spelling

Q1 a) their

b) there

c) where

d) whether

e) bought

f) quite

g) practice

h) effect

i) stationary

j) who's

Q2

Useful Words and Phrases for the Writing Question		
Starting a formal letter:	**Ending a formal letter:**	**Beginning a speech:**
Dear Sir / Madam Dear Mrs Jones	Yours sincerely Yours faithfully	Welcome Good evening
Persuasive phrases:	**Impersonal phrases**	**Phrases to link paragraphs**
We all know that What we should do now Surely we could	It can be argued Some people believe One point of view is	On the other hand A second reason for this is Another important concern is

Q3 <u>Occasionally</u>, I like to visit the centre of town. You can see all the <u>government</u> <u>buildings</u> which are really big and <u>impressive</u>. There are lots of <u>people</u> in the streets, walking and <u>laughing</u>. The <u>atmosphere's</u> brilliant. My favourite place is <u>definitely</u> the <u>cathedral</u> <u>which</u> is nine <u>hundred</u> years old. Inside the <u>cathedral</u> it's very cold but the <u>stained</u> glass <u>windows</u> are <u>beautiful</u>. There's also a coffee shop <u>there</u> which sells <u>delicious</u> cakes. <u>Separate</u> from the <u>cathedral</u> is a small chapel which is <u>notorious</u> for <u>having</u> nuns <u>buried</u> inside the walls.

Writing Answers

Writing — Writing for Different Purposes

Page 38 Writing for the Reader or Audience

Q1 A ii) The text describes what happened in a fairly impersonal style and quotes an eye-witness to the event.

B iv) The text uses simple language and explains a word ("algae") that the younger children might not understand.

C i) The text uses an informal tone and language as if writing to a friend, e.g. "blimey", "did I tell you", "bigger than Gavin's bike."

D iii) The text uses formal and respectful language, and acknowledges that the reader knows a lot about the subject.

Q2 *Possible answer:*

12, Dogbowl Street
Harrogate
12th February

Dear Kate,

It was really exciting when I went to the zoo yesterday — this mad little kid let her hamster out into the puma cage! We were just wandering around and we heard a rumpus, so we rushed over to join the crowd outside the puma cage. The hamster was on the puma's back. You couldn't see what was happening very well, but apparently it was collecting the puma's fur in its pouches. The hamster was saved though, and the puma was alright too.

See you soon,
Gillian

Page 39 Writing for the Reader or Audience

Q1 iii) The headteacher and possibly readers of the local paper.

Q2 *Possible answers:*

atmospheric — The description of the holiday destination should give the feeling of what it's like to be there.
fairly formal — The entries are going to be read by the headteacher and possibly local newspaper readers so they shouldn't be too informal.
positive — The entries are about your favourite destination so they should be trying to show it in a good light.
evocative — The writing should give a good description so the reader can imagine what the place is like.

Q3 e.g.
The food in Brittany is wonderful. My family had never tasted anything better. You don't have to stick to the old French food clichés like croissants and baguettes. Instead you can go to markets which sell fresh fruit and honey pies which are delicious for breakfast. Bernadette and Hervé, the French couple we stayed with, went to the market every day. The weather was gorgeous, so you could wander idly around the market looking at the exquisite food and getting a suntan.

Page 40 Different Types of Writing

Q1

Type of Writing	Typical format / structure	Typical style/tone
Formal letter	Begins with an address and "Dear" Ends with "Yours sincerely" or "Yours faithfully	Fairly formal and impersonal Written to specific reader(s)
Speech	Begins with a welcoming introduction, followed by paragraphs and conclusion.	Written as if speaking directly to audience
Article/report	Has a headline, sometimes written in columns	Informative and impersonal
Story	Standard format, in paragraphs, with a beginning, middle and end	Entertaining / imaginative
Leaflet	Headings breaking up text, pictures with captions	Informative or persuasive Usually fairly formal
Informal letter	Begins with "Dear..." Ends with informal sign-off, e.g. "Best wishes"	Personal, informal Written to specific reader(s)

Q2 *Possible answers:*

a) Striking Binman Arrested
A man was arrested in the city centre on Saturday for indecent exposure. Tim Hazelwood, a Thorncastle resident, marched through the city centre wearing a dustbin to raise publicity for the cause of binmen striking in the city.
The binmen are striking for better pay to reflect their unpleasant job and unsociable working hours. The council have so far refused to offer a pay increase, claiming that there are more worthy causes deserving the council's money.

b) Dear Sandy Johns MP,
I am writing to you on behalf of the Refuse Collector's Strike Association of Thorncastle. We would like to request your support in our struggle for better pay. Please consider the fact that the job that refuse collectors perform is both very important and unpleasant. In addition to this the hours which we work are unsociable. These factors should be recognised with better pay.
Yours sincerely,
Jo Smith

c) The Refuse Collector's Strike
The refuse collectors of Thorncastle have decided to take strike action for better pay. The council believes that while the binmen have a worthy case, so do many other workers and the council's funds are limited. Negotiations are ongoing, and as little disruption will be caused as possible.
What You Can Do To Help
As rubbish is not being collected, it is necessary for us all to take steps to keep Thorncastle clean. Keeping bin bags outside your house is unhygienic — the council urges all Thorncastle residents to take rubbish to the skip themselves.

Page 41 Formal and Informal Writing

Q1 The answer should be fairly formal. On the one hand the speech is going to be given to a local MP and so can't be too informal in tone. On the other hand, the speech needs to be "light-hearted" so it can't be too formal either.

Q2 a) Good afternoon everyone. I'm here to tell you about events which have been happening in the school during the last few weeks. I will then show you around the school. You will have the chance to talk to some of the pupils and will be given some refreshments.

b) Switzerland is very exciting. There are many activities you can do, for example snowboarding, skiing, walking and shopping. In Basle there are bears you can feed, although it is quite cruel that they are kept in captivity.

Writing Answers

c) The main lottery draw has been fixed three times in the last year, this newspaper can reveal. Our investigative reporter discovered that supporters of the governing party had won significant lottery sums on several different occasions.

Q3 *Possible answer:*

Dear Jo,

How are you? I was hoping you could give me some of your good advice. As you know, I've loved doing gymnastics for years and want to keep on doing it. However recently I've been stricken with rheumatism which is common among people as old as I am.

Before you retired, I seem to remember you spent some time as a homoeopathist. Do you have any recommendations for herbal remedies which might ease my pain and enable me to backflip again? I do hope you can help,

lots of love,

Bessie

Page 42 Writing to Inform, Explain and Describe

Q1 **i)** — it **explains** what to do
iii) — it **informs** the reader about what the place is like
v) — it **describes** the person and **explains** why they are important

Q2 a) 1, B
2, C
3, A

b) **1** — The text explains everything, e.g. "Orson Welles is a really important director." It doesn't assume that the audience have heard of the director or the film.
2 — The text assumes that the readers know a lot about the film already, e.g. it uses the phrase "as you know."
3 — The text acknowledges that the readers may know about the film, e.g. it uses the phrase "you have probably heard of."

Q3 *Example answer:*

My favourite film is called 'The Battle of Algiers' which was made in 1965 by the Italian director Gillo Pontecorvo. The film shows events in the Algerian Revolution which took place 1954-1962 against French colonial rule. It shows the cruelty of the French military, but also the devastation caused by terrorist bombs planted by the Algerian side.

One of the reasons I like the film is its documentary feel — it shows events in a very realistic way. There are no stars in the cast, and the black-and-white footage looks more like an old newsreel than a feature film. More importantly the film shows a very balanced view of the revolution — it isn't just propaganda for the winning side.

Page 43 Writing to Inform, Explain and Describe

Q1 a) In Normandy, there is a very beautiful valley called the Gorge Rancré. It has an unusually hot climate. This means that olive groves and vines can flourish there. Past the olive groves, there is a river which is known locally as the 'Devil's River'. The name originated in an ancient local myth that an animal had to be drowned in the river each year to keep the devil happy.

b) Henry VIII decided he wanted to get rid of Anne Boleyn because she had failed to bear him a son. This was important to Henry because he wanted a male heir to the throne. Therefore, charges of adultery were brought against Anne. These charges were probably untrue, but it didn't matter because Henry was so powerful. Anne was executed as a result.

Q2 a) exercises
b) delicious
c) incredibly
d) distant objects

Q3 a) The computer has a spell-checker which will find any incorrectly spelt words and help me change them.

b) My grandfather was an air-raid warden; he helped make sure people kept the black-out during air raids in World War II.

c) Liverpool is a multicultural city; people of many different cultures and faiths live there.

d) The striker was clearly offside — he had already run past all of the other players when the ball was passed to him.

Q4 *Possible answer:*

I rampaged over to the local funfair at the weekend. The rides were unbelievable. I tried the waltzer, but it made me feel unwell. Then I rode on the roller-coaster, and it was exhilarating. I loved going upside down and seeing all the people on the ground. When I got off the roller-coaster, I saw a friend from school but he disappeared before I could speak to him. Before I left, I devoured some candyfloss, which was gorgeous.

Page 44 Writing to Persuade, Argue and Advise

Q1 **i, iii, iv**

Q2 *Possible answers:*

a) People need to think about the effect smoking has on their health before they even try a cigarette.

b) The question we have to ask is, "If the government really has evidence about why we should eat spinach, why don't they tell us what it is?"

c) If you don't want to go on the trip, you should ask your mother to write a letter to the teacher explaining why.

Q3 *Possible answers:*

a) I enjoy swimming it is relaxing, fun and healthy.

b) It's important to read the newspapers because they are thought-provoking, informative and interesting.

c) We all know that homework is fascinating, inspiring and exciting.

Q4 *Possible answers:*

a) Perhaps you should take part in the race.

b) Maybe you could leave your job.

c) Would you like to come swimming at the leisure centre tomorrow?

d) Could you try to come to a decision soon?

Writing Answers

Page 45 Writing to Persuade, Argue and Advise

Q1 a) Paragraph (a) is not persuasive because it offers a fairly balanced view of the two candidates. It gives good points of both Claire Harris and Edward Jones.

b) Paragraph (b) is persuasive because it tries to persuade the reader that Claire Harris is the better candidate. It describes three of her good qualities for emphasis — that she is "intelligent, honest and cares about the local area." Her policies are praised, while in comparison her rival Edward Jones's track record is criticised.

Q2 a) The death penalty should not be reintroduced in Britain. There have been several recent cases in Britain where long-serving prisoners have been found innocent because of new evidence. If we had the death penalty in Britain these people would have been wrongly executed long ago. Lord Justice Hodgeman has said on this issue, "Although I have great faith in the British legal system, we should not lie to ourselves that it is infallible."

b) The death penalty should be reintroduced in Britain. Keeping people in prison costs the government money — for buildings, staff, food and healthcare. People who have committed horrific crimes and are sentenced to life imprisonment are wasting government resources. Re-introducing the death penalty would also act as a deterrent to criminals. It would show them that the legal system in Britain is strong and won't let them get away lightly with their crimes.

Q3 *Example answer:*

Despite protests from some parents and teachers, cars are still allowed in our school playground. This is a terrible hazard and we need to ask ourselves how much longer it can be allowed to continue.

The strongest argument against cars being allowed in the playground is that they are dangerous. Children run around in the playground, and the risk of an accident is high. There are several examples of children being run over and killed in school playgrounds. These tragedies are horrendous for the schools and families, and an appalling thing for other children to witness.

Some people argue that by driving slowly they can avoid having an accident. This is a misguided attitude. People are often killed or badly injured by cars driving as slowly as 20mph.

Another important reason for wanting to keep cars out of the playground is that they take up a lot of space. The playground is a useful area for children to run around, socialise and exercise. If they are kept in a small area of the playground then their breaktimes will be less healthy and stimulating.

In conclusion, teachers and parents who complain that there is no other space to park, or that their cars aren't safe elsewhere, aren't thinking about the safety and health of the children they claim to care for. We must support the campaign to keep cars out of the playground for good.

Page 46 Writing to Imagine, Explore and Entertain

Q1 iii) a gripping opening to the story

iv) development of the plot, characters and setting established in the opening.

ii) a crisis

i) a satisfying ending, which resolves the crisis

Q2 *Possible answers:*

a) Ilona turned to the headteacher furiously and screamed like a banshee.

b) As he crept over to the side of the ship, Bob's shoes squeaked like mice.

c) The atmosphere in the dentist's waiting room was like a funeral parlour.

d) The chips looked gorgeous. Henry was as hungry as a lion.

Q3 *Possible answers:*

a) Slashing rain set off a summer storm.

b) Cool, calm and collected, the cat crept through the casino.

Q4 *Possible answers:*

a) crash, bang, boom

b) screech, zoom, growl

Q5 *Possible answer:*

Then, making the whole situation worse — into the room marched my old nemesis Miss Rumpel! I was so shocked my entire body went numb. There was no chance of hiding, so I had to confront her. I took the catapult from my pocket, saying to myself, "It's not over until I'm given double detention for the next six years."

Q6 a) Henry — athletic, timid, fit, introverted

b) Mrs Henderson — intimidating, ancient, garrulous, authoritarian

c) Pau — fashionable, famous, glamorous, musical

Page 47 Writing to Imagine, Explore and Entertain

Q1 Paragraph **(ii)** is more suspenseful. This is because it withholds the information about what is in the bag until the end of the paragraph. Paragraph **(i)** lets you know what's in the bag straight away, so there isn't any suspense.

Q2 a) She was sitting quietly on a bench in the park. She didn't seem scared. I rushed up and said, "Run away — as fast as you can," but she didn't seem to understand.

b) The warrior Xenodwarf wielded his sword and yelled, "Enemy, prepare for death." To his surprise the enemy refused to surrender and did a nifty flying kick towards his right ear.

Q3 I was led through the servants' quarters towards the big kitchens. I felt scared, and couldn't stop my hands from shaking. The only time I'd been here before had been to deliver a message to my sister who worked here as a lady's maid. Even then, I'd been frightened. There were stories about the manor; people I knew in the village said there were so many corridors under the house it was like a maze. A boy had been lost down there, in a game of hide and seek. The rumour was that he was still alive.

Q4 *Example answer:*

Dear Claire,

That video you lent me got me into all sorts of trouble! I took it with me on my last voyage. After I'd learnt the basic moves, I found I was pretty good at it. The music was so infectiously jolly and toe-tapping. It reached the point though where I was finding it really difficult to steer the boat, because I was so busy dancing. I guess you could almost call it an addiction.

Writing Answers

Well, all was not lost, because what should I find under a life jacket but my favourite Bach CD. That CD saved me — I was so relieved to listen to something calm and classical. So three months later than expected, here I am back at home. Hope to see you soon dear — but you'd better not lend me any more videos!
Best wishes,
Sterling

Q5 *Example answer:*
July 14th
Gemma's wedding today was beautiful. I felt really proud of her. She let me be a bridesmaid which was fun — even if the dress I had to wear was horrific. My mum and dad really enjoyed the ceremony too, which I was relieved about because they were getting really stressed about all the arrangements.
I remember when I first met Gemma's fiancé Geoffrey, I wasn't sure whether I liked him. His musical taste was awful and he tried to make me laugh with jokes which weren't funny. To be honest, I still don't feel that I know him very well.
When I heard that they were getting married, I was a bit shocked. Gemma's only a few years older than me, but by getting married she seemed like an old woman. Now they're getting a mortgage on a house and Gemma's going to move out. I've never lived without my sister before, and the idea of it makes me feel a bit worried. I'll be left living with just my parents and that won't be as fun at all.

Page 48 Writing to Analyse, Review and Comment

Q1 a) Children over 14 should be allowed to go on holiday by themselves because they enjoy different holiday activities to their parents.

b) The advertising by confectionery and fast-food manufacturers on children's television persuades children to eat unhealthy food.

c) Few people are aware that the government is trying to introduce stealth taxes on mobile phones.

Q2 *Possible answers:*

a) Some people believe that the greenhouse effect is having a terrible effect on the Earth's environment.

b) One point of view is that if the Green Party got into power, it would be great for Britain and great for the environment.

c) Dogs often make very good pets, because they force people to go for walks and get some fresh air.

d) Trains are usually not on time.

Q3 *Example answer:*
Controversy Over Football Stadium Plans
There are arguments raging in Sudley about whether a new football stadium should be built in the centre of the city.
The managers of the local football club are pushing for the plans to go ahead. They argue that the stadium will be much bigger than the old one. This will allow more fans to watch the match, and also bring in more money.
However, not everyone is so keen. Some local residents are worried about the noise and traffic congestion which might be caused by placing the new stadium in the centre of town. There are also fears about football hooliganism.
Local shopkeepers and businesses support the idea though. They hope it will bring more people into the town centre. Pubs and food outlets in particular might profit.
The council are finding it hard to come to a decision about planning permission, when the people affected have such different points of view.

Page 49 Writing to Analyse, Review and Comment

Q1 *Possible answer:*
Arguments supporting YES
1. Tax-payers' money shouldn't be given to support a family who are already rich.
2. The members of the Royal Family are no different to anybody else — they just happen to have been born into a very rich and powerful family.
3. The monarch shouldn't be head of state, because they aren't elected. The Royal Family isn't democratic.
Arguments supporting NO
1. Tradition is important, the Royal Family have played an important role in the history of Britain.
2. The Royal Family play an important role as the figureheads of various charities and good causes.
3. The Royal Family are something famous about Britain. Their palaces and appearances attract tourism.

Q2 a) This conclusion is too vague, e.g. "It's a really difficult issue and it's hard to reach a conclusion." It fails to make a memorable statement about the issue and doesn't make the writer's viewpoint clear.

b) This is a good conclusion. It refers back to the bulk of the essay, gives the writer's viewpoint and ends on a strong statement. The tone is fairly impersonal and objective.

c) This conclusion doesn't work because it allows the writer's personal opinion to take over completely. This means that the tone of the writing becomes personal and subjective, e.g. "any other views are deeply misguided."

Q3 *Possible answer:*
The Royal Family are a really contentious issue. As discussed above, some people strongly believe that they still have a role in modern Britain while others see them as an out-dated drain on resources. I believe that the Royal Family should retain their traditional role as head of state, but with less privileges. For example some of the palaces could be given to the National Trust and be used to attract more tourism. However, any change would be a surprise, as at the moment the Royals seem as popular as ever.

Writing — Text Structure and Organisation

Page 50 Paragraphs

Q1 1 — a
2 — d
3 — c
4 — e
5 — b

Q2 Pompeii was a small city of no great importance in the Roman world. One of the few mentions it gets in ancient texts is in relation to a fight which broke out at the amphitheatre in which several people were killed. We can glean more information from the archaeological excavations at the site. From the size of the site it is estimated that it had about twenty thousand inhabitants.

Writing Answers

Evidence from the site includes: buildings, the contents of people's houses, wall paintings, graffiti and plaster casts of people who died in the explosion.

Q3 As Myrna sat down at the kitchen table she already felt full. So far she had eaten five blueberry tarts, ten Easter eggs, a rhubarb crumble and 76 fun-size chocolate bars.
Ali ran into the room and saw the last piece of evidence, the double-cream layered pavlova still there on the kitchen table.
"Come on, he's almost here!" he yelled.
"I'm trying," groaned Myrna.
Meanwhile, the dastardly Mr Smiker was walking slowly across the fields, his nose twitching in the breeze. The unmistakable scent of a missing double-cream layered pavlova filled his monstrous nostrils. He smiled a terrifying smile. Even his teeth were evil.

Page 51 Paragraphs

Q1 We all know that school buses are environmentally friendly. If our school bus was discontinued each child would have to travel to school individually. Seventy-five students make use of the bus service; that's a lot of extra cars. As the headteacher has said, "The pollution caused by the extra cars travelling to school would have a bad effect on the environment."

Q2 a) Some people are strongly against abortion.

b) Some people support a woman's right to have an abortion.

Q3 Once, when Hilary was at primary school, she'd climbed over the playing field fence. All her friends had run away because they were scared. Hilary had refused to be scared and had started walking as far from school as possible. After about two hours she had reached her own house. Hilary had been annoyed; she'd wanted to have an adventure, not to go home.

Q4 Paragraph (a) compares the two seasons better, because it gives some detail about each one. Paragraph (b) is almost all about winter, and gives very little detail about summer, so it isn't a proper comparison.

Q5 *Example answer:*
The activities you can do in cities and in the countryside are very different. Cities have lots of fun places to go, for example, museums, theatres and cinemas. In the countryside there aren't as many places like this. On the other hand there are lots of outdoor activities you can do, for example walking and horse-riding.

Page 52 Linking Paragraphs

Q1 furthermore, another point of view is, with hindsight, a contrasting view is, however, another example of, in addition to this, on the other hand

Q2 a) Nowadays, however, people know that white lead is dangerous.

b) On the other hand, the Parent's Association have a fairly moderate view.

c) However, the views of many parents about cartoons contrast strongly with those of their children.

Q3 *Example answer:*
When I was ten I lived in Newcastle. It's a big city, and you can get around it by Metro. In the area I lived, called Jesmond, there was a dene (park) you could run around which had a river and pet's corner.
While I was living in Newcastle, I went to school at 'All Saints' primary school. The school was in temporary accommodation, so most of the classrooms were in portacabins.

Q4 *Example answer:*
I think that fashion can be as outrageous as you want. What you wear shows what your personality is like. For example, I wear an Alkaline Trio hoodie that I got from one of their gigs because it's cool and it shows what music I'm into.
On the other hand, you could look at my parents' idea of fashion. They're really conformist and buy clothes from catalogues and Marks and Spencer. They wear their clothes for years. If they buy new clothes they always choose ones identical to what they had before.

Page 53 Writing Good Introductions

Q1 **ii)** Good evening
iv) We are here tonight to discuss
viii) Welcome
x) The key issue I am going to discuss is

Q2 Paragraph **i)** is persuasive. It argues clearly in favour of more security in schools. Paragraph **ii)** on the other hand describes different points of view as if they are equally valid — this would be appropriate for an analysing essay, but not for a persuasive essay.

Q3 *Example answer:*
The issue of whether advertising should be allowed on children's television is a controversial one. Many parents argue that the adverts should be banned, because they persuade their children to want expensive toys and unhealthy food. On the other hand, television executives argue that the money from advertising is spent producing good children's programming. They also point to the fact that many children enjoy watching adverts because of their imagination and humour. This essay will discuss both sides of the argument.

Q4 *Example answer:*
Bob was feeling happy. He had a date with Karen tonight down at the Rubics Cube club — it was the over-50s disco night so they could have two games for the price of one. He turned on some Tom Jones and opened the wardrobe to find his favourite viscose shirt. He blinked; he gulped. All his clothes were torn to shreds. Then, downstairs, he heard the noise. He began to jive his way nervously down the stairs.

Page 54 Structuring the Middle Bit

Q1 v) Introduction — outline your main argument.

i) Give a reason to support your argument. Back it up with evidence.

vi) Give a second reason to support you argument. Back it up with evidence.

iii) Give a reason why people might not agree with your argument. Give evidence of why they are wrong.

iv) Give a second reason why people might not agree with your argument. Give evidence of why they are wrong.

ii) Conclusion — bring together main points why your argument's right.

Writing Answers

Q2 Essay plan **ii)** is the worst structured of the three. It only gives advantages to living in the countryside, and doesn't comment on the disadvantages. Therefore it isn't a balanced essay, and appears to be biased towards living in the countryside.

Q3 ii), iii), i), iv)

Page 55 Structuring the Middle Bit

Q1 a) • The SATs will be over soon
• Hard work will be rewarded with good grades
• Pupils who don't work hard will regret it later.

b) *Example answer:*
The SATs Will Be Over Soon
• The SATs will be over in a week.
• There will be a long summer holiday soon.
All Your Hard Work Will Be Rewarded With Good Grades
• Hard work is the only way to guarantee good grades.
• It will make you feel a sense of achievement when you get good grades.
Pupils Who Don't Work Hard Will Regret It Later
• If you don't work hard, you won't get good grades
• You will feel like a nitwit when you get your results back.

Q2 *Example answer:*

a) Arguments supporting your point of view
• If a driver runs over a pedestrian when he's doing 20mph, there is a one in five chance they will be killed
• City speed limits are often as high as 30mph — the risk to lives is too high.
Opinions which disagree with your point of view
• People are often in a hurry, they don't want to slow down
• Improvements in traffic control and pedestrian crossings make the roads safer, and allow cars to go faster.

b) Arguments supporting your point of view
• Reducing the number of road deaths is much more important than people's need to travel to places quickly.
• Road accidents can be tragic, and cause a lot of pain and grief.
Opinions which disagree with your point of view
• Most drivers are responsible and would slow down if there was a hazard.
• The focus should be on punishing people who break the existing speed limits — they are the drivers who cause accidents. They would still go fast even if you reduced the speed limit.

c) Arguments supporting your point of view
3. If a driver runs over a pedestrian when he's doing 20mph, there is a one in five chance they will be killed
4. City speed limits are often as high as 30mph — the risk to lives is too high.
1. Reducing the number of road deaths is much more important than people's need to travel to places quickly.
2. Road accidents can be tragic, and cause a lot of pain and grief.
Opinions which disagree with your point of view
• ~~People are often in a hurry, they don't want to slow down~~
1. Improvements in traffic control and pedestrian crossings make the roads safer, and allow cars to go faster.
2. Most drivers are responsible and would slow down if there was a hazard.
3. The focus should be on punishing people who break the existing speed limits — they are the drivers who cause accidents. They would still go fast even if you reduced the speed limit.

Page 56 Pointing Out the Structure for the Reader

Q1 Introduction **ii)** signposts clearly what the structure of the leaflet is going to be. It says specifically which three areas are going to be covered by the leaflet.

Q2 ii) The second half of this essay will discuss the disadvantages...

iv) There are three main issues at stake here; they will be discussed in turn.

v) The first half of this essay will discuss the advantages...

vi) The second reason for supporting this point of view...

vii) Finally, this essay will consider the impact on...

Q3 A big argument in favour of the new sports hall is that it is a major facility that the school currently lacks. At the moment children have to travel to the local leisure centre to do P.E. and this is a waste of valuable lesson time.

A second important argument in favour of the new sports hall is that exercise is a really important part of education. It helps make people healthy and happy. It would be good if the school could offer a wider range of sporting activities and a new sports hall would enable this.

The second half of this essay will discuss the disadvantages to the new sports hall. Firstly, the proposed site for the new sports hall is far from ideal. The plan is to build it on the site of the old and beautiful school garden. Many people disagree with this strongly.

Another reason people don't want the school garden destroyed is that is the only place, other than the playground, where children can sit and relax at breaktimes. The importance of a peaceful place in a busy school cannot be dismissed lightly.

Page 57 Writing Good Conclusions

Q1 This statement is false. The conclusion should bring together the points made in the essay; it shouldn't bring in new information. It's also very important that the conclusion matches the tone and opinion of the rest of the essay.

Q2 **i)** a final statement about the topic
iii) a summary of the main points in your essay
viii) your own view on the topic

Q3 *Example answer:*
In conclusion, animal testing is cruel and often unnecessary. Testing causes pain to the animals. In the case of cosmetics testing this seems particularly unnecessary, as they could be tested on humans instead. Although there may be some worth in testing medicines, I still believe it should be kept to a minimum. Any unnecessary testing should be banned.

Q4 *Example answer:*
Velma picked up the axe, and walked down the stairs to the cellar. Bob slammed the door behind her and locked it. Velma yelled in indignation. He moonwalked to the phone and dialled 999. There was a crash as Velma swung the axe against the cellar door. Bob was green with fear.

Writing Answers

Then Karen walked in.
"Thank heavens you're here," cried Bob.
"What's the trouble?" said Karen.
Velma crashed through the cellar door. Karen whacked her over the head with her bowling ball.
"Come on Bob," said Karen, "we've got a date."

Writing — Practice Questions

Page 58 The Long Writing Question

Q1 a) **ii)** a mixture of teachers, pupils and parents

b) "Write an article for your school magazine"

Q2 a) formal, polite

b) It should be fairly formal because it is going to be read by parents and teachers, and is trying to discuss an issue seriously. It should be polite, because appearing angry and offensive won't help to persuade people round to your point of view. Teachers and parents are more likely to respond well to a polite, formal tone.

Q3 a) to persuade, argue or advise

b) It means that the purpose of the article is to argue in favour of one point of view and to persuade the readers that this view is right.

Page 59 The Long Writing Question

Q1 a) **ii)** homework is an important issue / I believe that / should pupils be given less homework?

b) Option **i)** is phrases suitable for a speech, not an article. Option **iii)** is too informal, plus you shouldn't insult people who don't agree with your view.

Option **iv)** is suitable for an informative essay, not a persuasive essay.
Option **ii)** is best because the tone is fairly formal, and the phrases are suitable for a persuasive article.

Q2 *Use the phrases from your answer to Q1 a) and some of your own, e.g.*
- We all know that
- We all need to think hard about
- The essay is going to argue that
- In conclusion

Q3 *Example answer:*

a)
- Homework makes pupils stressed and tired.
- Homework stops children from taking part in extra-curricular activities.

b)
- Teachers often set homework from habit, even if it isn't really necessary.
- Teachers often underestimate how long homework tasks will take pupils to do.

Q4 *Example answer:*

a)
- Homework lets pupils practise skills.
- Homework helps pupils learn information

b)
- Homework helps children learn the skill of working on their own, and managing work in their own time.
- It means revision for exams is easier, because the children will have learnt more during the year.

Page 60 The Long Writing Question

Q1 **a)-c)** *Example answer:*
<u>Reasons you agree/disagree with homework</u>
2. Homework makes pupils stressed and tired.
1. Homework stops children from taking part in extra-curricular activities.
~~• Teachers often set homework from habit, even if it isn't really necessary.~~
3. Teachers often underestimate how long homework tasks will take pupils to do. (3 goes with 1)

<u>Different opinions people might have about homework</u>
1. Homework lets pupils practise skills. (1 goes with 2)
2. Homework helps pupils learn information.
4. Homework helps children learn the skill of working on their own, and managing work in their own time.
3. It means revision for exams is easier, because the children will have learnt more during the year.

Q2 Options **i)** and **ii)** are both good. Option **iii)** isn't very good because it is always necessary to consider both points of view.

Q3 This statement is false. It's OK to change your argument but you should say you're doing it and mention it again in the conclusion.

Q4 *A good answer will:*
- *<u>Use the essay plan</u>:*
— discuss the points in the essay plan
— give priority to the points that are marked as the most important in the essay plan
— use some of the words and phrases in the 'words and phrases to begin and end your essay' box in the introduction and conclusion.
- *<u>Structure the essay well</u>:*
— clear introduction, middle paragraphs and conclusion
— structured middle section, e.g. points supporting your opinion discussed first, points against your opinion (and why they're wrong) discussed second.
- *<u>Make the essay flow well</u>:*
— link paragraphs together smoothly
— signpost the structure for the reader
- *<u>Use evidence to back up points</u>:*
— Each paragraph should have a clear point backed up with evidence, e.g. quotes, statistics, examples.
- *<u>Use correct punctuation, spelling and grammar</u>:*
— use a variety of punctuation correctly, e.g. question marks, apostrophes, exclamation marks and commas
— punctuate long sentences correctly using commas, semicolons or colons.
- *<u>Use interesting vocabulary and sentence structures</u>:*
— include some unusual and longer words
— use a variety of verbs
— vary length of sentences
— vary how you start sentences
- *<u>Use persuasive tricks</u>:*
— e.g. rhetorical questions, groups of three adjectives, use "we" and "us", be polite
- *<u>Use a tone suitable to the audience / reader</u>:*
— the article is for readers of the school magazine, including parents and teachers, so it should be fairly formal and polite in tone.
- *<u>Be about 300 words long</u>*

Q5 *I can't help you with this one, lazybones.*

Writing Answers

Page 61 The Short Writing Question

Q1 What is the purpose of this piece of writing?
to entertain and imagine
Who is going to read it?
readers of the local Herald newspaper
Write down three words which describe the tone you think the writing should have
Possible answers: lighthearted, informal, humorous

Q2 a) • the characters who are mistaken for each other and why they are so alike
• who mixes them up
• what the result of the mix up is

b) *Example answer:*
• the characters who are mistaken for each other and why they are so alike
— Shaun and Jason
— They are two brothers from Cheshire who look a bit alike. They're so boring people can't tell them apart.
• who mixes them up
— A mad professor called Pete who's been inventing a new type of witchcraft for three years.
• what the result of the mix up is
— Pete meets Shaun. He is so bored that he performs a spell to try and get rid of the boringness.
— Jason turns up.
— Pete thinks his spell's gone wrong and the boringness is expanding. He is so scared that he jumps in the canal.
— Jason and Shaun haul Pete out of the canal.
— They are in the local paper as heroes. No one thinks they're boring any more.

Q3 *A good answer will:*
• *Use the essay plan:*
— use the structure and ideas thought out in the essay plan
• *Structure the writing well:*
— write in paragraphs
— structure your story in an effective way, e.g. introduction, development of characters and situation, crisis, conclusion which resolves the crisis.
• *Make the essay flow well:*
— link paragraphs together smoothly
• *Use correct punctuation, spelling and grammar:*
— use a variety of punctuation correctly, e.g. question marks, apostrophes, exclamation marks and commas
— punctuate long sentences correctly using commas, semicolons or colons.
• *Use interesting vocabulary and sentence structures:*
— include some unusual and longer words
— use a variety of verbs
— vary length of sentences
— vary how you start sentences
• *Use tricks for good imaginative writing:*
— Build up atmosphere and mood, by using description and imagery, e.g. similes and metaphors, adjectives and adverbs, alliteration and onomatopoeia.
— Use suspense and surprise to keep the reader interested.
— Perhaps write from the point of view of one of the characters in the story.
— Avoid using clichés
• *Use a tone suitable to the audience and purpose of the writing:*
— e.g. lighthearted, inoffensive, humorous
• *Be about 200 words long*

Q4 *This one's up to you.*

Page 62 Revision Questions

Q1-3 *Good answers to these three questions will:*
• *Have completed a rough essay plan:*
— For Q1 and Q2 an essay plan based on the planning page provided should have been completed. It should include points made in the question, and your own ideas.
— For Q3 a rough plan should have been sketched out, including points made in the question.
• *The writing should use the essay plan:*
— discuss the points in the essay plan
— use the structure thought out in the essay plan
• *Structure the essay well:*
— clear introduction, middle paragraphs and conclusion
— structured middle section
• *Make the essay flow well:*
— link paragraphs together smoothly
— signpost the structure for the reader
• *Use evidence to back up points:*
— Each paragraph should have a clear point backed up with evidence, e.g. quotes, statistics, examples.
• *Use correct punctuation, spelling and grammar:*
— use a variety of punctuation correctly, e.g. question marks, apostrophes, exclamation marks and commas
— punctuate long sentences correctly using commas, semicolons or colons.
• *Use interesting vocabulary and sentence structures:*
— include some unusual and longer words
— use a variety of verbs
— vary length of sentences
— vary how you start sentences
• *Make the writing suitable for the writing purpose*
Q1 — a piece of informative writing
Q2 — a piece of analytical writing
Q3 — a piece of persuasive writing
• *Use a tone suitable to the audience / reader:*
Q1 — readers of a broadsheet newspaper
Q2 — pupils at your school
Q3 — managing director of local theatre
• *Be the right length*
— Q1 and Q2 are long writing questions, so they should be about 300 words long
— Q3 is a short writing question, so it should be about 200 words long.

Shakespeare Answers

Shakespeare — The Basics

N.B. All answers are merely suggestions — many alternatives are possible.

Page 63 Know Your Play

Q1 a) Romeo and Juliet

Act 1 Scene 1 — There is a huge fight between the Montagues and Capulets. The Prince warns everyone that he's had enough of the fighting. Romeo comes in and complains about love.

Act 1 Scene 2 — Paris persuades Lord Capulet to let him marry Juliet. Lord Capulet says it's OK with him but up to Juliet.

Act 1 Scene 3 — Lady Capulet tells Juliet that Paris wants to marry her, then they go to the party.

Act 1 Scene 4 — Romeo, Mercutio and Benvolio find out about the Capulet party and decide to gatecrash.

Act 1 Scene 5 — At the party, Romeo meets Juliet and they fall in love. Tybalt is angry with Romeo for gate crashing.

Act 2 Scene 1 — After the party, Romeo decides to break into the Capulet house again to go and see Juliet.

Act 2 Scene 2 — Romeo goes to talk to Juliet at her balcony. They say they love each other.

Act 2 Scene 3 — Romeo goes to talk to Friar Lawrence and convinces him that he loves Juliet and that Rosaline, his old crush, is history.

Act 2 Scene 4 — Romeo and Mercutio have a joking competition. The Nurse comes with a message from Juliet. Romeo tells the Nurse that he loves Juliet.

Act 2 Scene 5 — The Nurse tells Juliet that Romeo loves her and he has arranged for them to get married that afternoon.

Act 2 Scene 6 — Friar Lawrence is convinced that Romeo and Juliet should get married, so he marries them straight away.

Act 3 Scene 1 — Tybalt tries to fight Romeo. Romeo refuses because he doesn't want to fight Juliet's cousin, so Mercutio fights instead and is killed. Romeo is so angry that he kills Tybalt. As a punishment, the Prince exiles him.

Act 3 Scene 2 — Juliet finds out that Romeo killed Tybalt and has been banished. She doesn't know if she should be upset that Romeo killed Tybalt, upset that Romeo is banished, or glad that Tybalt didn't kill Romeo.

Act 3 Scene 3 — Romeo finds out he has been exiled, but says he would rather die than live without Juliet.

Act 3 Scene 4 — Lord Capulet secretly arranges for Juliet to get married to Paris.

Act 3 Scene 5 — Romeo goes to say goodbye to Juliet. Lady Capulet comes and tells Juliet she is going to marry Paris. Juliet refuses and Lord Capulet gets angry.

Act 4 Scene 1 — Juliet tells Friar Lawrence that she would rather die than marry Paris, so he hatches a plan for her to fake her own death by taking a sleeping potion.

Act 4 Scene 2 — Juliet goes home and pretends she wants to marry Paris.

Act 4 Scene 3 — Juliet takes a sleeping potion to make her appear dead.

Act 4 Scene 4 — Lord and Lady Capulet prepare for the wedding.

Act 4 Scene 5 — On the day of the wedding, Juliet appears to have died. Everyone is devastated and the wedding becomes a funeral.

Act 5 Scene 1 — Romeo hears that Juliet is dead. He buys some poison and heads back to Verona.

Act 5 Scene 2 — Friar Lawrence realises that a letter he sent to Romeo telling him that Juliet wasn't really dead wasn't delivered, so he sets off to break Juliet out of the tomb when she wakes up.

Act 5 Scene 3 — Romeo breaks into Juliet's tomb, but Paris spots him. They fight and Romeo kills Paris. Romeo finds Juliet and takes poison so he can die with her. Juliet wakes up, sees that Romeo is dead and stabs herself. Friar Lawrence arrives just too late. The watch arrive and the whole story is revealed.

The Tempest

Act 1 Scene 1 — The ship carrying Alonso and his followers is caught in a violent storm.

Act 1 Scene 2 — On the island, Prospero, who raised the storm with his magic, tells Miranda that, in the past, Antonio and Alonso robbed him of his title of Duke of Milan and set him and Miranda adrift at sea, with only Gonzalo helping them. Ferdinand arrives and he and Miranda fall in love straightaway, but Prospero decides to test their love and make things difficult for them.

Act 2 Scene 1 — Alonso believes Ferdinand must have drowned in the storm. Antonio persuades Sebastian to kill Alonso while he is sleeping, so that Sebastian can become King of Naples, but Ariel arrives just in time to stop them.

Act 2 Scene 2 — Trinculo meets Caliban when he tries to take shelter under Caliban's cloak. Stephano, who is drunk, finds them and gives Caliban some wine, and Caliban thinks Stephano must be a god.

Act 3 Scene 1 — Miranda comforts Ferdinand as he piles up logs as ordered by Prospero. Miranda and Ferdinand agree to get married.

Act 3 Scene 2 — Stephano, Trinculo and Caliban are all drunk, and Stephano beats up Trinculo when Ariel makes it seem that Trinculo is calling him a liar. Caliban tells Stephano that, if he kills Prospero, Stephano can have Miranda and be 'King of the island', and Stephano agrees to do it.

Act 3 Scene 3 — Ariel makes a magic banquet appear in front of Alonso and his followers, before making it suddenly vanish. He also tells them that the shipwreck was their punishment for throwing Prospero out of Milan. Alonso is sure Ferdinand is dead, and Gonzalo tries to keep everyone calm.

Act 4 Scene 1 — Prospero says Ferdinand and Miranda can get married and they watch some spirits perform a masque to celebrate. Then Prospero suddenly remembers the plot to kill him, and Prospero and Ariel chase off Caliban, Stephano and Trinculo.

Act 5 Scene 1 — Prospero casts a final spell on Alonso and his followers before forgiving them all, and revealing that Ferdinand is alive and engaged to Miranda. The Boatswain arrives and says the ship is fine, and Prospero invites them all back to his cave before they all set off home. Stephano, Trinculo and Caliban get told off and ordered to tidy Prospero's cave. Ariel is set free once he's arranged good weather for the journey.

Epilogue — Prospero asks for the audience's support on his journey back to Milan.

Shakespeare Answers

b) Romeo and Juliet
Act 1 — The Montague and Capulet families hate each other. Romeo is lovesick because the girl he loves, Rosaline, doesn't love him back. Romeo meets Juliet for the first time at the Capulets' party and falls in love with her straight away.
Act 2 — Romeo breaks into the Capulets' mansion and finds out that Juliet loves him. They declare their love for each other and promise to stay in touch. At the end of the scene they get married.
Act 3 — Mercutio is killed by Tybalt so Romeo kills Tybalt in revenge. Romeo is exiled but says that he would rather die. Juliet is told that she has to marry Paris.
Act 4 — Juliet says she would rather die than marry Paris. Friar Lawrence hatches a plan so that Juliet can fake her own death, then escape to be with Romeo. Juliet pretends to want to marry Paris, but then takes a sleeping potion to make herself appear dead.
Act 5 — Romeo hears that Juliet is dead. He rushes back to Verona with a plan to poison himself. Friar Lawrence had sent a letter to Romeo telling him about the plan but it never arrived. When Romeo reaches Juliet's tomb, Paris tries to stop him getting in, so Romeo kills him. Romeo poisons himself and dies. Juliet wakes up just as Friar Lawrence arrives, sees that Romeo is dead and kills herself to die with him. Everyone arrives and Friar Lawrence tells them all what happened. The Capulets and Montagues give up the feud.

The Tempest
Act 1 — Alonso and his followers are caught in a storm and washed up on a remote island. Prospero tells Miranda that Alonso and Antonio betrayed him in the past, and Miranda and Ferdinand fall in love.
Act 2 — Antonio and Sebastian plot to kill Alonso. Trinculo, Caliban and Stephano meet.
Act 3 — Miranda and Ferdinand agree to marry, and Caliban persuades Stephano to kill Prospero. Ariel plays a magic trick on Alonso and his followers.
Act 4 — Prospero says Miranda and Ferdinand can get married, then goes off to deal with Caliban, Stephano and Trinculo.
Act 5 — Prospero forgives his enemies and gives up his magic. The characters prepare to set off home.

Q2, Q3, Q4 *Answers to these questions depend on which play you're studying.*

Q5 a) A long section of a play
b) A shorter section of a play — part of an act
c) One of the people in the play
d) A play that ends badly for the main character
e) A play that is funny or has a happy ending
f) A play based on real people from the past
g) A group of words with a set rhythm
h) A long bit of talking by one person
i) Part of a sentence
j) Any dialogue that's not poetry — normal speech
k) Dialogue in separate lines with a rhythm
l) The rhythm of poetry
m) When a character leaves the stage
n) When all of the characters present leave the stage
o) When a character says something that the other characters can't hear

Page 64 Understanding the Language

Q1
thy — your
ere — before
thee — you
thou wilt — you will
hither — to here
he hath — he has
hie — go
thou art — you are
thou hast — you have
wherefore — why
hence — from here
thou — you

Q2 a) conjurations — story / illusion
felon — crime / criminal
b) outstrip — be better than, surpass
c) saucy — rude
scathe — injure
contrary — contradict
d) prosper — make good time / have a super journey
Tunis — Tunisia (a place)
paragon — perfect example

Page 65 Understanding the Language

Q1 Possible answer:
• ALONSO I don't want to hear this. I wish I had never let my daughter get married there (in Tunis), because on the journey I have lost my son, and at the same time my daughter is so far away from Italy that I'll probably never see her again. Oh my son, and heir of Naples and Milan, I wonder which fish ate you when you drowned.

Q2 Possible answer:
• ROMEO You can't talk about something you have no experience of. If you were my age, and had gone through everything I have, then you could say what you think. You could roll on the ground like me wishing you were dead.

Q3 Possible answer:
• PROSPERO Look, it's me, Prospero — the man who was Duke of Milan but had it stolen from him. If you need more proof that it's me, I'm going to hug you, and warmly welcome you and your friends.

Q4 *This answer depends on which play you're doing.*

Shakespeare Answers

Page 66 Backing Up Your Answers

Q1 a) • "good Capulet, which name I tender as dearly as mine own"

b) • "if you should deal double with her, truly it were an ill thing to be offered to any gentlewoman"

c) • "most wicked sir, whom to call brother Would even infect my mouth, I do forgive"

d) • "villain"

e) • "moonshine"
• "green sour ringlets"
• "the ewe"
• "midnight mushrooms"
• "noontide sun"
• "mutinous winds"
• "green sea"
• "azured vault"

Page 67 Backing Up Your Answers

Q1 a) • "Lo, here upon thy cheek"

b) • "thou mayst brain him"
• "Batter his skull"
• "paunch him with a stake"
• "cut his wezand with thy knife"

c) • "O, the heavens!"

d) • "Put not another sin upon my head"
• "think upon these gone"

Page 68 Writing Your Answers

Q1 a) i) Yes

ii) • Who wrote hit after hit after hit

iii) If the works were hits then lots of people must have gone to see the plays.

b) i) • Lords, ladies and gents all rated his skills
• hit after hit after hit

ii) Repetition

iii) Repetition makes him sound even more popular — "lords, ladies and gents" sounds like all the important people liked Kit and "hit after hit" suggests an unlimited number of hits.

c) The writer says the geese didn't like Kit because he used the geese's feathers as quills to write his plays — "Each day he used up forty goose-feather quills".

Q2 Possible answer:
• The writer says that the play was like "a grand opera and a fireworks display rolled into one". This makes the play sound lavish like an opera and spectacular like a fireworks display.
• The fact that the writer says "Luke Matchett *lived* the title role" makes it sound as if he was doing more than acting and so was very convincing in the role.
• The writer says that Caliban was "suitably evil", but the actor managed to convey an "underlying sadness". The fact that she's describing the actor doing two things at once shows that she's impressed.
• At the end of the review, the writer calls the play "An absolute triumph!". This is quite an over-the-top way of saying the performance was good so it shows she is really enthusiastic about it.

Page 69 Writing Your Answers

Q1 a) • Romeo and Juliet love each other despite their families being enemies; "doff thy name, / And for thy name, which is no part of thee, / Take all myself". This shows that their love is more important to them than loyalty to their parents; "My name, dear saint, is hateful to myself, / Because it is an enemy to thee".

b)

Point	Quote
Names play an important part in Romeo and Juliet.	"What's in a name?"
Juliet would love Romeo if he abandoned his family.	"doff thy name, and for thy name, which is no part of thee, / Take all myself."
Romeo hates his name.	"My name, dear saint, is hateful to myself, / Because it is an enemy to thee."
Juliet wasn't expecting to hear Romeo.	"What man art thou that thus bescreened in night / So stumblest on my counsel?"

c) • The atmosphere in this extract is very romantic. Romeo and Juliet talk about abandoning their family ties so that they can be together. The use of poetic language, for example the sweet smelling rose, and "call me but love" give the impression that what we are seeing is true love, and very romantic.

Shakespeare — Character Questions

Page 70 What Characters Do

Q1 a) Romeo— good with words, romantic
Juliet — romantic, has a good reputation
Prospero — powerful, has a temper

b) Romeo
Good with words — he declares his love for Juliet.
Romantic — he is lovesick at the start of the play. He also climbs the mansion walls to go and see Juliet and says he loves her even though they have only met once.
Juliet
Romantic — refuses to marry Paris because she doesn't love him, and talks from her balcony about her love for Romeo.
Has a good reputation — Paris and Romeo both love her, and her parents are aristocrats and two of the most important people in Verona.
Prospero
Powerful — he uses his magic to create the storm.
Has a temper — he treats Ariel and Caliban very harshly at times.

Q2 a) "I've thought of a plan, but it's dangerous."
"If you are strong enough to die rather than marry Paris..."
"...then you'd be prepared to face death if it solved your problem."
"If you dare to do it, then I'll help."

b) This extract suggests that Friar Lawrence is a wise and cunning man, as he quickly comes up with a solution to Juliet's problem. He is happy to help Juliet against the wishes of her family — which shows that he is loyal to her and Romeo. But he is also deceitful, as his plan for Juliet involves her faking her own death.

Shakespeare Answers

Page 71 What Characters Say

Q1 a) A — Caliban says that he used to be treated better, and that rightfully the island is his.
B — Caliban wants to have a party.

b) A — "This island's mine, by Sycorax my mother".

c) A — Caliban says that the island was his before Prospero took it off him.

Q2 a) A — Prospero talks about how he and Miranda were banished from Milan.
B — Prospero says he forgives Antonio and Sebastian for betraying him and plotting against Alonso.

b)
- forgiving
- determined
- moral

Q3 a) A — Men who are about to die are often happy.
B — Death has taken your breath, but you still have your beauty, so it hasn't won yet.

b)
- eloquent
- romantic
- determined

Page 72 What Characters Say

Q1 a) i) Alonso is pessimistic. — He feels sure Ferdinand is dead.
ii) Alonso feels guilty. — He blames himself for what's happened to Ferdinand.
iii) Alonso is irritable. — He's annoyed when people try to cheer him up.

b) i)
- "My son is lost"
- "What strange fish / Hath made his meal on thee?"

ii) "Would I had never / Married my daughter there, for coming thence / My son is lost."
iii) "You cram these words into mine ears against / The stomach of my sense."

Q2 a) i) Juliet has been feeling down lately — "to put thee from thy heaviness,"

ii) Lady Capulet is happily surprised by the idea. — "...a sudden day of joy, / That thou expects not, nor I looked not for."

iii) Juliet's dad has worked hard to get the wedding sorted quickly. — "thou hast a careful father, child, / One who... / Hath sorted out a sudden day of joy"

iv) Juliet feels reluctant to marry Paris. — "He shall not make me there a joyful bride."

Page 73 What Characters Say

Q1 *Here's one way you could complete the table:*

Comment	Explanation	Quote
Romeo is ungrateful for all the luck he's had recently.	Friar Lawrence tells him he and Juliet are both alive and well, and his life is saved.	"A pack of blessings lights upon thy back.".
Romeo has been saved from execution even though he killed Tybalt.	As a murderer, Romeo should have been executed.	"The law that threatened death becomes thy friend / And turns it to exile."
Romeo wanted to be dead for Juliet's sake.	Romeo wanted to die rather than be exiled away from Juliet.	"Thy Juliet is alive / For whose dear sake thou wast but lately dead."

Q2 *These are just a few of the things you could say:*

Comment	Explanation	Quote
Prospero treats Caliban harshly.	He threatens him with painful punishments.	"thou shalt have cramps, / Side-stiches that shall pen thy breath up"
In the past, Prospero was kind to Caliban.	He fed him well and taught him to speak.	"wouldst give me / Water with berries in't, and teach me how / To name the bigger light and how the less"
Caliban is bitter at Prospero.	He says Prospero stole the island from him.	"This island's mine by Sycorax my mother, / Which thou tak'st from me."

Q3 *The answer to this one depends on which character you choose.*

Page 74 How Characters Think

Q1 a) He tells him to fetch some fuel.

b) Because he doesn't do it straightaway.

c) Because he is scared of the power of Prospero's magic.

Q2 A — ii)
B — iii)
C — i)

Q3 a)
- "thou most lying slave"
- "stripes may move"
- "Filth as thou art"

b) He tried to violate (attack) Miranda.

Shakespeare — Language Questions

Page 75 Writing About Descriptions

Q1 a) Something big is going to happen tonight.
The party tonight will end badly.
God's in charge of my life course, he'll do what he wants.
Let's get going.

b) Any two valid answers, e.g.
- "I fear, too early, for my mind misgives / Some consequence yet hanging in the stars."
- "bitterly begin his fearful date / With this night's revels"

c) Any valid answer, e.g.
- "Direct my sail!"
- "Some consequence yet hanging in the stars"

d) He says that God is steering his course and there is nothing he (Romeo) can do about it, so they may as well get going.

e) *The answers a)-d) should be used, in any order, to answer the question.*

Q2 *These are just some of the points you could make in your answer. Don't forget the quotes:*
- The Prince uses several phrases which suggest that the families have fought before; "Rebellious subjects", "enemies to peace".
- The Prince says that they have "thrice disturbed the quiet of our streets" and talks about "Three civil brawls". This suggests that there have been several fights recently.
- The Prince says that Verona's citizens have had to take up weapons to stop the fighting, which suggests that the fighting normally happens in public places, and that it is very serious and violent.
- The Prince has to shout to be heard; "Will they not hear?", which suggests that the fighters are more interested in their fight than the law.

Shakespeare Answers

Page 76 Writing About Imagery

Q1 **A:**

a) Passionate love

b) Explosions / fire and gunpowder

c) It is unpredictable and dangerous.

d) Friar Lawrence is a bit worried about what is going to happen to Romeo and Juliet's relationship in the future.

e) The image adds a sense of tension to the scene — it makes the audience feel that something bad could happen at any time, like the explosion of a barrel of gunpowder.

B:

a) Sword fighting

b) Playing a musical instrument.

c) It is energetic, and can be unpleasant, like badly played music.

d) Mercutio is angry and wants to fight Tybalt and make him dance around, or dodge his sword for insulting him.

e) This scene brings out the hatred felt between the Montagues and the Capulets, and the violent nature of the feud. Mercutio is a close friend of the Montagues.

C:

a) Caliban, Stephano and Trinculo, and how they will be tormented.

b) Leopards

c) They will be covered in spots from the painful magic spells, and in pain from cramps.

d) Prospero is determined to punish them for plotting against him.

e) It adds to our impression of the power of Prospero's magic, and also shows how merciless he can be when he is angry.

Q2 *4 points similar to these should get 8 marks.*

• The phrase "A rotten carcass of a butt" suggests a decaying and dangerous boat, not fit for the Duke of Milan. This would add to the sense that the people who overthrew Prospero were evil and heartless.

• The imagery of the rats leaving the boat gives the impression of even more danger — the little boat wasn't only small and unpleasant but must have been dangerous as well if the rats had abandoned it.

• The "crying" and "roaring" of the sea adds to the tension and danger of the story; the danger that Prospero is describing makes his story even more dramatic.

• The description of the winds as "sighing" and the description of them as taking pity on Prospero gives the impression that the elements were on his side. This adds to the sense of magic in the scene — Prospero must be a really powerful wizard to be able to change and control the weather.

Page 77 Writing About the Mood

Q1 These are just a few things you could say.

	Setting	How the characters speak	Description & imagery	MOOD
A	The island	They speak in prose. Trinculo and Caliban insult each other a lot.	Trinculo calls Caliban a "monster" and a "natural".	Comical, aggressive
B	Juliet's room	Juliet is talking to herself. She is talking in riddles, which shows she is confused.	"I am not I if there be such an 'ay'" She talks about being "tortured".	Depressed, confused
C	Outside the Capulet's house.	Mercutio is playing with words, speaking in riddles and pretending to be a wizard.	"I must conjure him. I conjure thee by / Rosaline's bright eyes"	Comical, magical, mystical, over dramatic

---

Q2 *Use all the points you made in Q1 and don't forget to quote to back up everything you say.*

Page 78 Writing About Persuasive Language

Q1 Says it will be very simple to kill Alonso:

• "If he were that which now he's like — that's dead —
Whom I with this obedient steel, three inches of it,
Can lay to bed for ever"

Scoffs at the idea of feeling guilty:

• "Twenty consciences
That stand 'twixt me and Milan, candied be they,
And melt, ere they molest!"

Says Gonzalo won't be a problem:

• "This ancient morsel, this Sir Prudence, who
Should not upbraid our course."

Says no one else will stand in their way:

• "For all the rest,
They'll take suggestion as a cat laps milk,
They'll tell the clock to any business that
We say befits the hour."

Q2 Uses rhetorical questions:

• "Shall I speak ill of him that is my husband?"

Stands up to insults:

• "Blistered be thy tongue / For such a wish!"

Uses violent language to emphasise her emotions:

• "O what a beast I was to chide at him!"
• "Blistered be thy tongue / For such a wish!"

Romantic language

• "He was not born to shame"
• "Sole monarch of the universal earth"
• "'tis a throne where honour may be crowned"

Insists Romeo is honourable

• "Upon his brow shame is ashamed to sit!"
• "'tis a throne where honour may be crowned"
• "He was not born to shame"
• "Shall I speak ill of him that is my husband?"

Q3 *Whichever one you do, try to make as many points (backed up by quotes) as you can. You need to make at least six points (with quotes) to get full marks.*

Shakespeare Answers

Page 79 Revision Questions — Romeo and Juliet

Q1 a) *e.g.*
- "Villain"
- "Boy"
- "the injuries / That thou hast done me"
- "O calm, dishonourable, vile submission!"
- "Alla Stoccata"
- "one of your nine lives"
- "dry-beat the rest of the eight"

b) i) • Romeo is trying to avoid fighting Tybalt. He argues that "I love thee better than thou canst devise".
• Tybalt is angry with Romeo and refuses to accept his apology; "this shalt not excuse the injuries / That thou hast done me", but doesn't understand why Mercutio is angry; "What wouldst thou have with me?"
• Mercutio is angry with Tybalt for trying to fight Romeo, and with Romeo for trying to back out of the fight; "O calm, dishonourable, vile submission!"
ii) • Mercutio talks about drawing his sword; "Will you pluck your sword out of his pilcher by the ears?" and his sword being "about your ears". This gives us a description of sword fighting style, which creates some tension in the scene — we know the fight is serious.
iii) • Mercutio keeps using 'cat' references ("rat-catcher, King of cats"), which gives us the impression that Tybalt is cunning and violent.

iv) • Romeo uses long and thoughtful sentences in this extract, which suggests that he is calm and trying to reason with Tybalt.

• Tybalt and Mercutio use short, sharp sentences, full of emotive and violent language, showing that they are worked up into a violent frenzy.

v) • Romeo speaks in a more controlled rhythm, using longer sentences with more beats per line, showing that he is calm.
• Tybalt and Mercutio's rhythm is sharp and edgy, giving their lines a violent and tense edge.

c) *If any of your quotes from a) aren't used in b) add a point for each one.*

d) *Put the points in a sensible order. If there are any that don't really answer the question leave them out. If you think other points need to be made to answer the question, add them in.*

e) *Use your plan from part d). You need to make at least six points with quotes to get full marks.*

Page 80 Revision Questions — The Tempest

Q1 a) *e.g.*
- "printless foot"
- "the ebbing Neptune"
- "demi-puppets"
- "moonshine"
- "green sour ringlets"
- "midnight mushrooms"
- "azured vault"
- "potent art"
- "heavenly music"
- "airy charm"

b) i) • Prospero is remembering all the powerful magical spells he has cast in the past. Now he feels ready to give up his magic for good.

ii) • The description of "ye that on the sands with printless foot / Do chase the ebbing Neptune" gives the speech a mythical feel, as it sounds like a fairy tale or a legend rather than real life.
• The phrases "dread rattling thunder" and "Jove's stout oak" create a sense of the formidable power of nature, adding to the impression of how powerful Prospero's magic must be to be able to control them.
iii) • The imagery of "azured vault" to describe the sky gives an impression of its vastness and its deep blue colour.
iv) • Prospero's sentences are mostly long and complex. This allows him to list all the magical beings he has power over. The long sentences sound impressive and mystical, adding to the mysterious, magical mood.
v) • The rhythm is slow and steady, allowing Prospero to sound commanding and powerful, gradually building up an impression of the range and power of his magic.

c) *If any of your quotes from a) aren't used in b) add a point for each one, e.g.:*
• Mythical creatures such as "elves" and "demi-puppets" set the scene for the magical, unbelievable events that Prospero describes.
• Prospero's powers sometimes seem to extend even to waking the dead, as in "Graves at my command / Have waked their sleepers".
• The "moonshine" suggests that the events happen at night, with the glow of the moon creating a spooky, magical atmosphere.

d) *Put the points in a sensible order. If there are any that don't really answer the question leave them out. If you think other points need to be made to answer the question add them in.*

e) *Use your plan from part d). You need to make at least six points with quotes to get full marks.*

Q2 a) e.g. The two key parts of the question here are 'closeness' and 'distance'. The words and phrases chosen to answer the question here should fall into these two categories:

Closeness:
- "My dear one"
- "I have done nothing but in care of thee."
- "Wipe thine eyes. Have comfort."

Distance:
- "You [...] left me to a bootless inquisition"
- "Stay, not yet."
- "Obey"

b) i) • Prospero feels it is time to tell Miranda about her past: "'Tis time / I should inform thee farther." He wants her to know how much his daughter means to him : "I have done nothing but in care of thee [...] my dear one," He wants her to understand his actions and realise that he's more powerful than she thinks: "I am more better / Than Prospero, master of a full poor cell,"
• In the past Miranda has felt rejected: "You have often [...] left me to a bootless inquisition, / Concluding 'Stay, not yet.'" But, she hadn't wanted to hurt her father by asking difficult questions: " More to know / Did never meddle with my thoughts." Miranda is ready to hear the truth. She loves her father and does as he asks.

Shakespeare Answers

ii) Descriptions in this passage are short and concise and quickly get to the point because Prospero is keen for Miranda to know about what he has to say.
• Prospero describes their home as a "full poor cell" to emphasise how he hates being stuck on the island. It shows that he wants Miranda to realise that it wasn't his choice to live there.
• Prospero also highlights the "direful spectacle of the wreck", to show how awful the shipwreck looked.
• Miranda has very little opportunity to be descriptive as her father is very much in control of the conversation. This is a technique Shakespeare uses to show the control that Prospero has over his daughter both in language and in life.
iii) • Miranda uses the imagery of the "bootless inquisition" to stress how strongly she feels about her father's inability to talk to her in the past.
iv) • Miranda's sentences are short because her father is very much in control of the conversation. He steers the conversation, jumping from one explanation to another as he is keen for Miranda to hear his story.
v) • The pace of the passage is steady. Prospero is careful to explain things fully to his daughter and he is keen not to miss out any key details.

c) *If any of your quotes from a) aren't used in b) add a point for each one.*

d) *Put the points in a sensible order. If there are any that don't really answer the question leave them out. If you think other points need to be made to answer the question add them in.*

e) *Use your plan from part d). You need to make at least six points with quotes to get full marks.*

Shakespeare — Performance Questions

Page 81 Performance — The Basics

Q1 a) • "They are both in either's pow'rs, but this swift business
I must uneasy make, lest too light winning
Make the prize light."

b) thoughtful, quiet

c) forceful, loud, angry, accusatory

Q2 • At the start of the extract, Romeo is his usual calm but highly emotional self. He uses phrases such as "good, gentle youth", which in turn make Romeo seem gentle, but the phrase "tempt not a desperate man" adds an edge of tension to the scene.

- Romeo becomes more desperate sounding through the passage, begging Paris to give up and leave; "Put not another sin upon my head, / By urging me to fury".
- When Paris refuses to let Romeo pass and tries to arrest him, Romeo instantly loses his temper. He doesn't even give Paris a second chance, but attacks him viciously; "have at thee, boy!" This really shows how desperate and emotional Romeo is in this extract.

Page 82 How Characters Speak

Q1 a,b) *"Affection makes him false, he speaks not true"*
• annoyed — she is annoyed that a friend of the Montagues is trying to shift the blame onto Tybalt.
• accusing — she is basically saying he is lying to protect the Montagues.
"Romeo must not live"
• assertive — she is stating the law and wants justice. Tybalt is dead, so Romeo should legally be executed.
"The life of Tybalt"
• pleading — he's trying to protect Romeo by trying to convince the Prince that Romeo was only acting on behalf of the law when he killed Tybalt, who had killed Mercutio.
*"I have an interest in your hearts' proceeding;
My blood for your rude brawls doth lie a-bleeding"*
• regretful — The Prince has lost a relative to someone else's family feud.
• threatening— the Prince wants revenge for Mercutio's death.
"I'll be deaf to all pleading and excuses"
• remorseless — he feels no pity for his decision
• single-minded, determined
"that hour is his last"
• single-minded, determined — he must uphold the law and won't be bullied into submission, so he has to be ruthless.
• threatening — there is no doubt that if Romeo is found the Prince will have him killed.

Q2 *You could say something like this:*
• *"O good Gonzalo ... word and deed!"*
He could emphasise his gratitude and good will towards Gonzalo by speaking clearly and slowly.
• *"Most cruelly ... furtherer in the act"*
He should sound angry and reproachful, to emphasise his bitterness about what Alonso and Sebastian did. He should sound calm though, as he has had plenty of time to think about what happened.
• *"Thou art pinched for't now, Sebastian!"*
Prospero could raise his voice at this point, perhaps emphasising the word "pinched", to show his satisfaction that Sebastian is being punished for what he did.
• *"Flesh and blood ... unnatural though thou art."*
Prospero would again sound angry, but could also have a disbelieving, incredulous tone, to show he is still shocked and hurt that his own brother could betray him.
• *"Their understanding ... or would know me."*
Prospero would have a fairly neutral tone for these lines, as he is simply commenting on the fact that his enemies are coming back to their senses after the spell.
• *"Ariel, / Fetch me the hat and rapier in my cell."*
He should sound slightly more urgent and businesslike at this point, as he is about to put into place the final part of his plan — he wants to be in the clothes he wore when he was Duke of Milan, so that his appearance in front of his enemies has maximum effect.

Shakespeare Answers

Page 83 How Characters Move

Q1 a) • *"The fringed curtains of thine eyes advance"*
Prospero should point and Miranda should look in the same direction.
• *"Lord, how it looks about!"*
Ferdinand should be wandering around, looking for something.

b) • When Prospero says "No, wench", he could turn back to Miranda, and speak sternly (like a teacher) as he is giving Miranda a lecture on Ferdinand. He might pretend to sound a bit sad though, as if he feels sympathy for Ferdinand's loss.
• When Prospero says "stained / With grief", Ferdinand could continue to look around the stage for the people in the shipwreck, and look upset and tired. He could even show his sadness somehow, for example by sitting down and crying with his head in his hands.

Q2 • Juliet could hold up Romeo's hand as if she is admiring it when she says "For saints have hands that pilgrims' hands do touch."
• When Romeo says "let lips do what hands do", he could hold Juliet's hand, as if he is going to kiss it, maybe he could even bow down to it to show his devotion to her.
• When Romeo says "move not while my prayer's effect I take", he could get down on his knees to kiss Juliet's hand, as if he was praying. Juliet could even look a bit embarrassed at this point; it's an unusual thing for someone to do, after all.

Q3 • When Prospero says the words "foul conspiracy" he could have a disgusted expression on his face, to show his contempt for Caliban and his fellow plotters.
• When Prospero says "Well done! Avoid", he could turn towards the spirits who have been acting in the masque, and possibly gesture impatiently for them to go away, to show he needs to deal with Caliban as quickly as possible.
• Ferdinand should frown in confusion when he says "This is strange", to emphasise his surprise at Prospero's sudden change in mood.
• Miranda could have a worried expression on her face at seeing him "so distempered", to show she is concerned because Prospero doesn't usually act like this.

Page 84 Revision Questions — Romeo and Juliet

Q1a) • 1st chunk — Romeo says — Let me die, I'm happy. I'll tell you that it's not morning yet, and it's not the lark who is singing. I'd rather stay than go. Come on death, Juliet wants you to have me! Let's talk for a bit longer, it's not morning.
• 2nd chunk — Juliet says — It's morning, go! It is the lark that's singing. Some say that her song is a lovely tune, but it's tearing us apart and hunting you down. Go away before it gets light. Romeo comments that the lighter it gets, the bigger their problems are.
• 3rd chunk — the Nurse arrives and tells Romeo and Juliet that Lady Capulet is coming, so Romeo escapes.

b) Juliet:
i) • 2nd chunk — Romeo
• 3rd chunk — Nurse
ii) • 2nd chunk — Juliet is desperate that Romeo should escape and live; "O now be gone, more light and light it grows".
iii) • 2nd chunk — Juliet could be pacing around and trying to shoo Romeo away at this point.
• 3rd chunk — Juliet could be looking surprised — she's not expecting to see the Nurse, who bursts in in a hurry.
iv) • 2nd chunk — Juliet should be sounding upset, and maybe slightly desperate because she wants Romeo to leave and not be caught.
• 3rd chunk — surprised to see the Nurse.
v) • 2nd chunk — Juliet needs Romeo to leave. The second time she tells him this she should be sounding even more desperate and hurried than the first. She could increase her physical actions, waving him off or hurrying him towards the exit; "hence, be gone, away!" "O now be gone."

Romeo:
i) • 1st and 2nd chunk — to Juliet.
ii) • Romeo is confused — he knows he should go into exile but he wants to stay with Juliet; "I have more care to stay than will to go".
• 2nd chunk — Romeo is feeling distraught here, and is quite upset that he has to leave; " more dark and dark our woes".
iii) • 1st chunk — He could be looking out of the window at the sun rising to show that he is worried and that he knows he has to go. Maybe he could turn to Juliet when he says "Let's talk"
• 2nd chunk — he could look Juliet in the eye and sound upset, so that the audience really feel his pain.
iv) • all chunks — he could sound either calm or hysterical, but either way he should sound upset since he knows he has to leave but doesn't want to.
v) • 1st chunk — Romeo is desperate to stay with Juliet, his tone of voice should lighten as he imagines there is still time for them to talk. His actions could also reflect his desire to stay; he could approach Juliet or enter further into the room.
"How is't, my soul? Let's talk, it is not yet day".
• 2nd chunk — none.

Nurse:
i) • 3rd chunk — everyone.
ii) • 3rd chunk — nervous and tense; "be wary, look about".
iii) • 3rd chunk — As the stage direction says, the Nurse should enter hastily, perhaps still preparing for the day, tying her apron for example.
iv) • 3rd chunk — As the stage direction says, the Nurse should enter hastily. She should speak in a way that shows this — she could be flustered, for example.
v) • 3rd chunk — The nurse cares for Juliet and warns her of danger. She should sound caring yet forceful in the double warning she offers Juliet. She may have a worried face. She could help speed up Juliet's preparation for her mother's arrival by tidying the room or helping her to dress; "be wary, look about."

Shakespeare Answers

c) *Try to use as many points from b) as you can in your answer. You need to make at least six points with quotes to get full marks.*

Page 85 Revision Questions — The Tempest

Q1 *This is the kind of thing you could include in your answer:*

i) In this extract, Ariel is talking to Prospero, who is giving him orders to fetch some spirits to perform a show.
ii) • Prospero is feeling excited, and wants Ariel to hurry; "ARIEL: Presently? / PROSPERO: Ay, with a twink."
• Ariel should support this. He sounds slightly magical in this extract, suggesting that he is also a bit excited about the play; "Before you can say 'come' and 'go'... / Do you love me, master? No?"
• This shows that both characters are feeling quite happy and playful. Ariel is Prospero's servant, but he feels that he can have some fun with him.
iii) • For the line "what would my potent master", Ariel might appear quickly on stage. Prospero has been calling Ariel, so he should look like he's in a hurry.
• Ariel's poem ("before you can say 'come' and 'go'"), is quite light hearted and rhythmical, so Ariel might be dancing or swaying in time with the poem here.
iv) • When Ariel first appears, Prospero has been calling him, so he could sound slightly out of breath, as if he as been rushing to get to Prospero, or maybe he could sound curious, because he wants to know what Prospero wants him to do. He calls Prospero "my potent master", so he might sound grand or humble here. When he says his poem though, he could sound happy and excited, since he is joking around.
v) • The actor playing Ariel could end the speech with a flourish when he says the words "Well! I conceive.", nodding to show that he knows what Prospero wants him to do.
• For the lines that begin "Do you love me", Ariel's voice could become a bit pleading, as he is looking for a compliment.

Q2 *This is the kind of thing you could think about for your answer:*

Trinculo
i) To himself
ii) He's bemused by Caliban — he's only just worked out that he's a person and not a fish. He's concerned about taking shelter from the storm — "there is no other shelter hereabout".
iii) He could leap back from Caliban when he says "Warm, o' my troth!", to show he is startled to find out Caliban is alive. When he creeps under Caliban's cloak, he could do so tentatively, to show he is wary of him.
iv) He should sound nervous and unsure of what the best thing to do is. When he says "this is no fish, but an islander", he could sound shocked at the discovery.
v) "o' my troth!"

Stephano
i) He is singing and talking to himself.
ii) He is drunk and seems amused by the discovery of Caliban — "Have we devils here?".
iii) He could stagger about from side to side to show how drunk he is. When he drinks he should swig the wine straight from the bottle, possibly spilling some down his chin.
iv) He should slur his words quite a lot. When he finds Caliban he should sound quite excited and intrigued, as he can't work out what he is at first. When he says "I have not scaped drowning to be afeard now of your four legs", he should sound assured and defiant, to show he is not afraid.
v) "devils", "Ha!"

Caliban
i) In his first line he is pleading with Stephano. In his second line he is talking to himself.
ii) He feels frightened and doesn't know what is happening — "Do not torment me."
iii) He could cower under his cloak, hiding his head, to show he is afraid and trying to avoid being seen.
iv) He could speak in a high-pitched shriek, or his voice could be shaking with fear.
v) "O!"

Shakespeare — Ideas, Themes and Issues

Page 86 Ideas, Themes and Issues in Romeo and Juliet

Q1 a,b) • *"'Tis but thy name that is my enemy,"*
Juliet is saying that it is only Romeo's name that makes him an enemy of her family, not himself.
• *"What's Montague?"*
Juliet is asking what it means to be a Montague that makes you different from any other person.
• *"O be some other name!"*
Julet is saying that if Romeo had any other surname she could be with him.
• *"What's in a name?"*
Juliet is asking why your name makes you different from any other person.
• *"doff thy name"*
Juliet is asking Romeo to abandon his name so that they can be together.

c) • Juliet seems to recognise that names mean something, but she does not seem to think that they are more important than actual feelings. They are a way of identifying yourself, nothing more.

d) • Shakespeare may be suggesting that there is more to a person than their family.
• He may also be suggesting that people's opinions of each other based on their names can be unfair.

Q2 *These are some of the things you could write about.*

a, b) • *"A gentler judgement vanished from his lips, / Not body's death, but body's banishment."*
This suggests that Friar Lawrence thinks that being alive but in exile is better than being executed.
• *"Ha, banishment! Be merciful, say 'death'"*
Romeo thinks that being forced to live in exile is worse than death.
• *"There is no world without Verona walls /... And world's exile is death."*
Romeo is saying that exile is a form of hell, a slow, painful death.

Shakespeare Answers

c) • Friar Lawrence thinks that exile is a great outcome for Romeo, when he could have been killed. He tells Romeo that "the world is broad and wide", meaning that there will be new opportunities for Romeo.
• Romeo thinks that life outside of Verona is meaningless because everything he knows and loves is there. Living somewhere else would be like losing his soul — he would rather die and get it over with.

d) • Shakespeare seems to suggest that some things aren't worth living for, and that sometimes death is an easier option.
• He also seems to be suggesting that there are two kinds of death — physical death and emotional death.
You need to make at least 6 points properly backed up with quotes to get 18 marks.

Page 87 Ideas, Themes and Issues in The Tempest

Q1 a,b) • *"the sea, which hath requit it"*
The sea has avenged the betrayal of Prospero by bringing his enemies to the island.
• *"The pow'rs, delaying, not forgetting, have*
Incensed the seas and shores, yea, all the creatures,
Against your peace."
Fate is not going to let Alonso and his followers escape punishment for their crimes.
• *"Thee of thy son, Alonso,*
They have bereft, and do pronounce by me
Ling'ring perdition, worse than any death
Can be at once, shall step by step attend
You and your ways"
Ariel announces that fate is punishing Alonso by taking his son away from him and leading him into eternal ruin.
• *"heart's sorrow,*
And a clear life ensuing"
Alonso will be left to reflect on his actions, in order to clear his conscience.

c) • Ariel is saying that all the problems and disasters that have befallen Alonso since the shipwreck are a direct punishment for how he treated Prospero in the past. He says that fate is ensuring that justice is done.

d) • Shakespeare seems to be saying that, no matter how long people think they have got away with doing something bad, justice will always be done in the end.

Q2 a,b) • *"Your charm so strongly works 'em*
That if you now beheld them your affections
Would become tender."
Ariel says that, if Prospero could see how much his enemies are suffering from his spells, he would feel really sorry for them.
• *"Hast thou, which art but air, a touch, a feeling*
Of their afflictions, and shall not myself,
One of their kind, that relish all as sharply,
Passion as they, be kindlier moved than thou art?"
Prospero says that, if Ariel, who is only a spirit of the air, can feel sorry for them, then he, as a human being, should feel even more sympathy.
• *"Though with their high wrongs I am struck to th' quick,*
Yet with my nobler reason 'gainst my fury
Do I take part. The rarer action is
In virtue than in vengeance."
Even though Prospero is still angry about how he was betrayed, he's determined to be reasonable and not be ruled by his negative feelings. He says it is more honourable to forgive than to take revenge.
• *"They being penitent,*
The sole drift of my purpose doth extend
Not a frown further."
Prospero says that, if his enemies are sorry for what they've done, then his plan is complete and he doesn't need to punish them any more.

c) • Prospero values forgiveness more highly than revenge. He thinks that, if people are sorry for their bad deeds, they should be forgiven, not punished repeatedly.

d) • Shakespeare shows that it is possible to forgive your enemies, no matter how badly they have treated you in the past.
• He suggests that the noblest thing to do is to forgive, rather than take revenge.

Page 88 Ideas, Themes and Issues

Q1 a,b) • *"Draw, if you be men. Gregory, remember thy washing blow."*
Sampson is encouraging the Montagues to fight with him. He says that they're cowards if they won't draw their swords. He gives Gregory instructions to fight well — to remember his slashing blow. This also serves as a threat to the Capulets that Gregory is a good fighter.
• *"What, art thou drawn among these heartless hinds?*
Turn thee, Benvolio, look upon thy death."
Tybalt is insulting the Montagues. He uses alliteration (*heartless hinds*) to emphasise what he's saying. He threatens to kill Benvolio because Benvolio has his sword drawn.
• *"I do but keep the peace. Put up thy sword,*
Or manage it to part these men with me."
This shows that not everybody wants to keep the feud going — Benvolio is trying to stop the two sides from fighting. He tells Tybalt that he's trying to keep them apart, and asks him to either put his sword down, or use it to help keep the peace.
• *"Clubs, bills, and partisans! Strike! Beat them down!*
Down with the Capulets! Down with the Montagues!"
One of the citizens is encouraging others to get involved with the fight. He calls for them to grab their weapons. He uses short sentences that make it sound like he's angry and shouting.
• *"As I hate hell, all Montagues, and thee:"*
Tybalt states clearly that he hates the word peace as much as he hates hell and the Montague family.

c) • Tybalt is angry because Benvolio has his sword drawn. Tybalt's hatred for the Montagues is shown in the fact that he clearly doesn't trust them — he thinks that Benvolio is threatening him, even though Benvolio says he's trying to stop the others from fighting. Tybalt obviously takes the feud very seriously — he says that he hates the Montagues as much as he hates hell.

Shakespeare Answers

d) • Shakespeare shows that the feud is very violent and has been going on for a long time — both sides insult each other and are willing to fight. By including the citizens in the fight he shows how the feud is very public, and affects everybody in the city. The fact that the citizen shouts *"Down with the Capulets! Down with the Montagues!"* shows that the citizens aren't taking sides, but they're angry that the hatred between the two families has been disturbing the peace for such a long time. This emphasises how long the feud has lasted, and how difficult it would be for Romeo and Juliet to be together.

Q2 a,b) There is a constant struggle for power in this passage between Caliban and Prospero, who both claim that they own the island.

Caliban:

• *"This island's mine, by Sycorax my mother, / Which thou tak'st from me."*
Caliban says here that the island belongs to him because it was handed down to him by his mother, Sycorax. He believes Prospero has taken the island from him.

• *"Thou strok'st me and made much of me"*
Caliban says that Prospero looked after him and taught him things. This was perhaps part of Prospero's plan to win power over the monster, by making the monster feel that he was dependent on him.

• *"I loved thee, / And showed thee all the qualities o' th'isle"*
Caliban says that they were once friends. Prospero looked after Caliban and in return Caliban showed Prospero how to survive on the island.

• *"...and here you sty me"*
Now Prospero keeps Caliban shut up in a cave like a prisoner.

Prospero:

• *"lying slave, / Whom stripes may move, not kindness!"*
Prospero calls Caliban a slave who can only be controlled with a whip.

• *"I have used thee, / Filth as thou art, with human care, and lodged thee / In mine own cell"*
Prospero insists that he has treated Caliban with human kindness and taken him into his home. He doesn't seem to think that there is anything unnatural about their relationship as master and slave. He believes he deserves to be in charge.

c) Caliban feels used and unfairly treated. He used to be King of his own island. He has seen what it is like to have power and what it is like to live as someone's slave. As a result he challenges Prospero.
Prospero thinks that he is naturally superior to Caliban, who he doesn't even think is human. He says that he has treated Caliban with respect and tries to put him back in his place as a servant. Prospero refuses to give up his position of authority.

d) Shakespeare shows that power, like magic, is an illusion. Prospero seems to be powerful, but there are limits to his powers. His rule is limited to the island. He can only conjure the storm with the help of others and he only has power over people because they allow him to rule.